D1460236

Practice Papers for SQA Exams

Higher

Chemistry

© 2015 Leckie & Leckie Ltd

001/10042015

10 9 8 7 6 5 4 3

ISBN 9780007590933

Published by
Leckie & Leckie Ltd
An imprint of HarperCollins*Publishers*
Westerhill Road, Bishopbriggs, Glasgow, G64 2QT
T: 0844 576 8126   F: 0844 576 8131
leckieandleckie@harpercollins.co.uk
www.leckieandleckie.co.uk

Publisher: Peter Dennis
Project manager: Craig Balfour

Special thanks to
Helen Bleck (copy edit)
Jennifer Richards (proofread)
Louise Robb (proofread)
Keren McGill (editorial)
Lee Haworth Mulvey (editorial)
QBS (layout & illustration)
Ink Tank (cover)

A CIP Catalogue record for this book is available
from the British Library.

Acknowledgements
P24 © Steve Lagreca / Shutterstock.com

Introduction

Layout of the book

This book contains three practice papers, which mirror the actual SQA exam as closely as possible in question style, level and layout. It is the perfect way to familiarise yourself with what the exam papers you will sit will look like.

The answer section at the back of the book contains worked answers to questions, letting you know exactly where the marks are gained in an answer and how the right answer is arrived at. It also includes practical tips on how to tackle certain types of questions, details of how marks are awarded and advice on just what the examiners will be looking for.

How to use this book

The practice papers can be used in one of two ways:

1. You can complete an entire practice paper under exam conditions and mark it using the answer section. If you complete a practice paper this way it is important to make a list of all the key areas that you are having difficulty with by referring to the topic index at the front of the book, and concentrating your study time on these areas before attempting the next practice paper.

2. You can use the topic index to tackle a key area one at a time. This allows you to focus on specific key areas that you particularly want to revise. It also allows you to revise exam-style questions for just the topics you have covered.

Transfer your knowledge

As well as using your class notes and textbooks to revise, these practice papers will also be a useful revision tool as they will help you to get used to answering exam-style questions. As you work through the questions you may find that they refer to a case study or an example that you haven't come across before. Don't worry! You should be able to transfer your knowledge of a topic or theme to a new example. The enhanced answer section at the back will demonstrate how to read and interpret the question to identify the topic being examined and how to apply your course knowledge in order to answer the question successfully.

Command words

In the practice papers and in the exam itself, a number of command words will be used in the questions. These command words are used to show you how you should answer a question – some words indicate that you should write more than others. If you familiarise yourself with these command words, it will help you to structure your answers more effectively.

Command Word	Meaning/Explanation
Name, state, identify, list	Giving a list is acceptable here – as a general rule you will get one mark for each point you give.
Suggest	Give more than a list – perhaps a proposal or an idea.
Outline	Give a brief description or overview of what you are talking about .
Describe	Give more detail than you would in an outline, and use examples where you can.
Explain	Discuss why an action has been taken or an outcome reached – what are the reasons and/or processes behind it.
Justify	Give reasons for your answer, stating why you have taken an action or reached a particular conclusion.
Define	Give the meaning of the term.
Compare	Give the key features of 2 different items or ideas and discuss their similarities and/or their differences.

In the exam

Watch your time and pace yourself carefully. Work out roughly how much time you can spend on each answer and try to stick to this.

Be clear before the exam what the instructions are likely to be, e.g. how many questions you should answer in each section. The practice papers will help you to become familiar with the exam's instructions.

Read the question thoroughly before you begin to answer it – make sure you know exactly what the question is asking you to do. If the question is in sections, e.g. 15a, 15b, 15c, etc, make sure that you can answer each section before you start writing.

Question types

Each paper is composed of several question types.

Knowledge-type questions include:

- Accurate recall

- Apply knowledge

- Explain

Skill-type questions include:

- Select information

- Present information

- Process information

- Design experiments

- Evaluate procedures

- Draw conclusions

- Make predictions

In addition, there will be two open questions per paper.

Open questions

Each exam paper has two open questions and each is worth 3 marks. You can recognise an open question as it will contain the expression '**Using your knowledge of chemistry**'. In this type of question you are required to draw on your understanding of key chemical principles in order to solve a problem or challenge. The 'open-ended' nature of these questions is such that there is no one correct answer. These questions provide you with the opportunity to be creative, and reward analytical thinking. Feel free to include diagrams to help explain your answer fully. The answer sections provide some suggestions of answers that you may include but these lists are not exhaustive and if your answer is not included within these lists it does not mean that it is incorrect.

Topic index

SQA Unit	Paper 1		Paper 2		Paper 3	
Unit 1 – Chemical change and structure	**Section 1 questions**	**Section 2 questions**	**Section 1 questions**	**Section 2 questions**	**Section 1 questions**	**Section 2 questions**
Controlling the rate	4, 5, 6	15(a)	2, 3	3(b), 3(c), 15	1, 2	4
Periodicity	1, 2	1(b), 1(c), 1(d), 5(a)	4, 7	2	4, 5, 6	8(b), 12(a), 16
Structure and bonding		1(a), 1(e)	1, 5, 6	7(a), 13(a)	3, 7	2(a), 6(c), 15(b)
Unit 2 – Nature's chemistry						
Esters, fats and oils	7		9, 10	4(a), 4(bi), 6(a), 7(b), 8(a), 8(b), 12(c)	9, 10, 13, 15	3
Proteins	11, 12	15(b)	12	1	10, 14	1
Chemistry of cooking	3, 10	7, 16(a), 16(b), 16(ci)	8, 11	6(b)		9(b), 10(a)
Oxidation of food	8, 9		13	10(ai), 12(b)	11, 12	10(b)
Soaps, detergents and emulsions						
Fragrances		14(a), 14(b)				
Skin care		14(c)		16		14
Unit 3 – Chemistry in society						
Getting the most from reactants		5(b), 6(a), 6(b), 10b(i), 13, 17(b)	17	4(bii), 5(b), 10(b), 13(bii)	8, 19	7(b), 7(c), 12(b), 12(c), 13(c), 15(a), 15(c)
Equilibrium	13, 14	17(bii)	14, 15	12(a)	18	13(a), 13(b)
Chemical energy	17	2(c), 9(b), 11(a)	17, 18, 19	6(c)	16, 17	1(e), 5, 9(a)

Oxidising or reducing agents	15, 16, 18	9(a), 10(bii)	16	5(a), 13(bi)		6(a)
Chemical analysis	19, 20	10, 11(b), 15(c), 16(d)	20	3(a), 5(c)	20	7(a), 13(cii)
Open questions	3 and 8		9 and 11		2(b) and 11	
Skills	2(a), 2(b), 4, 6(c), 9(bii), 12, 15c, 16(bii), 17(a), 17(biii)		8(c), 10(aii), 14		6(b), 8(a), 10(c)	

SECTION 1 ANSWER GRID

Mark the correct answer as shown ◉

	A	B	C	D
1	○	○	○	○
2	○	○	○	○
3	○	○	○	○
4	○	○	○	○
5	○	○	○	○
6	○	○	○	○
7	○	○	○	○
8	○	○	○	○
9	○	○	○	○
10	○	○	○	○
11	○	○	○	○
12	○	○	○	○
13	○	○	○	○
14	○	○	○	○
15	○	○	○	○
16	○	○	○	○
17	○	○	○	○
18	○	○	○	○
19	○	○	○	○
20	○	○	○	○

Practice Exam 1

CfE Higher Chemistry

Practice Papers for SQA Exams

Exam 1

Fill in these boxes and read what is printed below.

Full name of centre

Town

Forename(s)

Surname

Try to answer all of the questions in the time allowed.

Total marks – 100

Section 1 – 20 marks

Section 2 – 80 marks

Read all questions carefully before attempting.

You have 2 hours to complete this paper.

Write your answers in the spaces provided, including all of your working.

Scotland's leading educational publishers

SECTION 1 – 20 marks

Attempt ALL questions

Answers should be given on the separate answer sheet provided.

1. Which of the following compounds has the **greatest** ionic character?

   A Sodium fluoride

   B Calcium fluoride

   C Potassium fluoride

   D Magnesium fluoride

2. What is the equation for the first ionisation of calcium?

   A $Ca(s) \longrightarrow Ca^+(s) + e^-$

   B $Ca(g) \longrightarrow Ca^+(g) + e^-$

   C $Ca(s) \longrightarrow Ca^{2+}(s) + 2e^-$

   D $Ca(g) \longrightarrow Ca^{2+}(g) + 2e^-$

3. Which of the following substances is most likely to be soluble in carbon tetrachloride (CCl_4)?

   A Phosphorus chloride

   B Calcium chloride

   C Sodium chloride

   D Caesium chloride

4. Which line in the table correctly represents the graph shown?

	Activation energy (kJ mol^{-1})	Enthalpy change
A	180	Exothermic
B	180	Endothermic
C	100	Exothermic
D	100	Endothermic

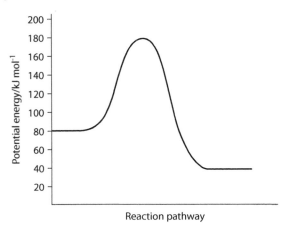

Reaction pathway

5. In which of the following will **both** changes result in a decrease in the rate of a chemical reaction?

A An increase in activation energy and an increase in the frequency of collisions.

B An increase in activation energy and a decrease in the frequency of collisions.

C A decrease in activation energy and an increase in the frequency of collisions.

D A decrease in activation energy and a decrease in the frequency of collisions.

6. The graph below shows the change in the amount of product produced in a chemical reaction with time.

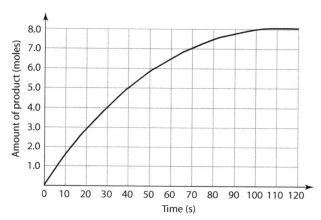

Calculate the relative rate of this reaction, in s^{-1}, at 30 seconds.

A 0·03

B 0·13

C 0·25

D 7·5

7. Shown below is the structure of aspirin.

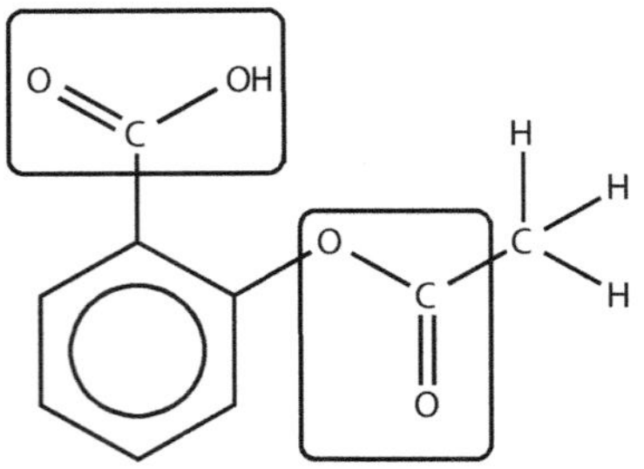

Which of the following are the correct names of the two functional groups highlighted?

A Carboxyl and ester link

B Hydroxyl and carbonyl

C Hydroxyl and carboxyl

D Ester link and carbonyl

8. Which of the following alcohols is a tertiary alcohol?

A

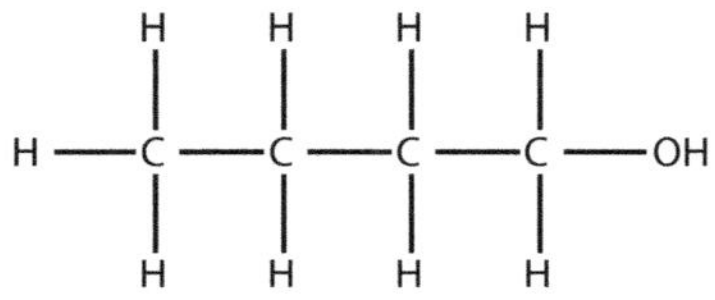

C

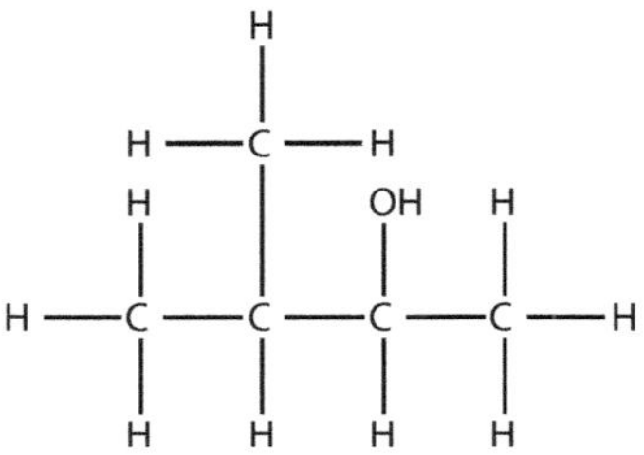

B

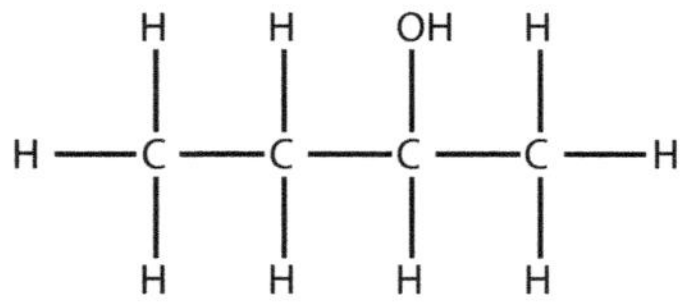

D

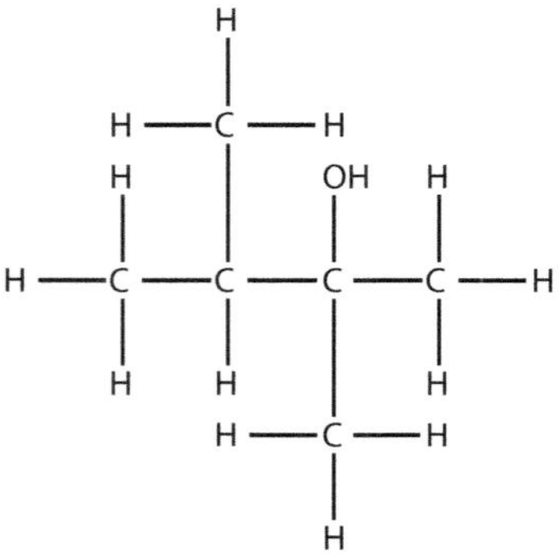

9. An alcohol is oxidised, using the oxidising agent acidified potassium dichromate, to produce the compound with the following structure:

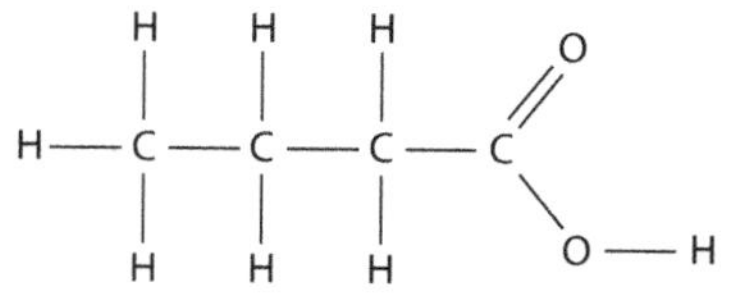

What alcohol was oxidised to produce this compound?

A Propan-1-ol

B Propan-2-ol

C Butan-1-ol

D Butan-2-ol

10. Glyceryl trioleate is a typical ester found in oils.

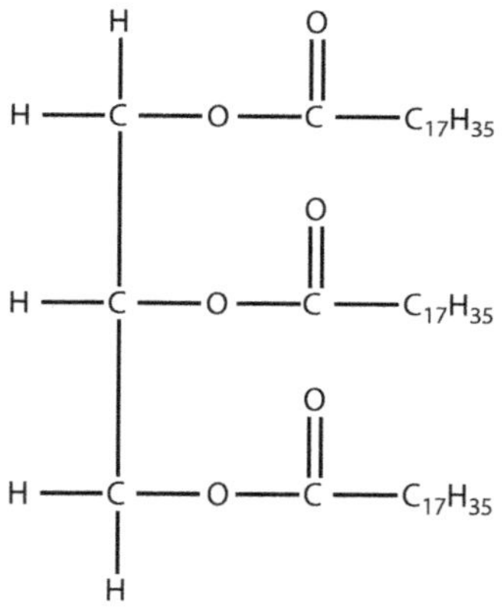

Hydrolysis of this compound produces 3 molecules of oleic acid and 1 molecule of

A propan-2-ol

B stearic acid

C glycerol

D glucose.

11. Enzyme molecules can be classified as

   A alcohols

   B proteins

   C esters

   D fats.

12. During digestion, proteins are broken down by hydrolysis.
What bond is broken during the hydrolysis of a protein?

   A C–C

   B C=O

   C C–N

   D N–H

13. Which of the following correctly states the effect that adding a catalyst will have on a reaction mixture at equilibrium?

   A The ΔH of the reverse reaction will increase.

   B The ΔH of the forward reaction will increase.

   C The position of equilibrium is unchanged.

   D The position of equilibrium always shifts to the right.

14. Iodine monochloride and chlorine gas react together to establish the following equilibrium in a closed system.

$$ICl(\ell) + Cl_2(g) \rightleftharpoons ICl_3(s) \qquad \Delta H = -106 \text{ kJ mol}^{-1}$$

Which line in the table shows the conditions that would cause the greatest increase in the amount of ICl_3 produced in this reaction?

	Pressure	Temperature
A	High	High
B	Low	Low
C	High	Low
D	Low	High

15. During a redox process, chlorate ions are converted into chlorine.

$$CIO_3^- \longrightarrow Cl_2$$

The reaction is carried out in acidic conditions to provide H^+ ions.

The number of H^+ ions required to balance this ion–electron equation is

A 12

B 10

C 8

D 6.

16. In which of the following reactions is hydrogen acting as an oxidising agent?

A $C_4H_8 + H_2 \longrightarrow C_4H_{10}$

B $2K + H_2 \longrightarrow 2KH$

C $S + H_2 \longrightarrow H_2S$

D $C_4H_6 + H_2 \longrightarrow C_4H_8$

17. 310 kJ of energy was released when 10 g of propan-1-ol (formula mass = 60 g) was burned.

Using this information, the enthalpy of combustion of propan-1-ol in kJ mol^{-1} is

A −155

B −1550

C −1860

D −3100.

18. Which of the following elements is the strongest oxidising agent?

A Oxygen

B Fluorine

C Chlorine

D Aluminium

19. Carbon dioxide gas is produced when chalk and acid react together. Which of the following combinations of equipment shown would provide the most accurate way of measuring the volume of carbon dioxide gas produced by the reaction?

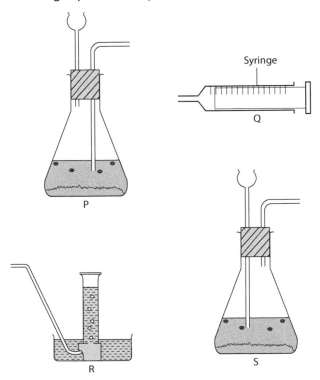

A P and Q

B S and Q

C P and R

D S and R

20. Which of the following procedures would be best for obtaining sodium chloride from a mixture of sodium chloride and silver chloride?

A Add water, filter and collect residue.

B Add water, filter and evaporate filtrate.

C Add hydrochloric acid, filter and collect residue.

D Add sodium hydroxide solution, filter and evaporate residue.

SECTION 2 – 80 marks

Attempt ALL questions

1. The first 20 elements of the periodic table can be categorised according to their bonding and structure.

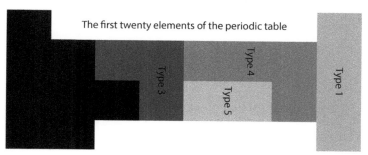

The first twenty elements of the periodic table

(a) Complete the following table by adding the type number to indicate where each type of bonding and structure can be found in the periodic table.

Type	Bonding and structure at room temperature
	Metallic lattice solids
	Covalent network solids
	Covalent molecular gases
	Monatomic gases
	Discrete molecular solids

2

(b) State which type contains the element with the greatest attraction for electrons in a covalent bond.

1

(c) Which type contains elements with no known electronegativity values?

1

(d) **Explain fully** why electronegativity values decrease going down a group of the periodic table.

2

MARKS

DO NOT
WRITE IN
THIS
MARGIN

(continued)

(e) Diamond and fullerene are well known forms of the element carbon. State how the structure of fullerene differs from that of diamond.

1

2. The rocket propellant dinitrogen tetroxide was developed in the 1950s.

In rockets it reacts with methylhydrazine.

$$5N_2O_4 + 4CH_3NHNH_2 \longrightarrow \mathbf{X}CO_2 + \mathbf{Y}N_2 + \mathbf{Z}H_2O$$

(methylhydrazine)

(a) Draw the full structural formula of methylhydrazine.

1

(b) Balance the above equation by giving the values of X, Y and Z.

1

(c) The equations for the combustion of methylhydrazine, carbon and hydrogen are:

$$CH_3NHNH_2(\ell) + 2\frac{1}{2}O_2(g) \longrightarrow CO_2(g) + N_2(g) + 3H_2O(\ell) \quad \Delta H = -1304 \text{ kJ mol}^{-1}$$

$$C(s) + O_2(g) \longrightarrow CO_2(g) \quad \Delta H = -394 \text{ kJ mol}^{-1}$$

$$H_2(g) + \frac{1}{2}O_2(g) \longrightarrow H_2O(\ell) \quad \Delta H = -286 \text{ kJ mol}^{-1}$$

Use this information to calculate the enthalpy change for the following reaction:

$$C(s) + N_2(g) + 3H_2(g) \longrightarrow CH_3NHNH_2(\ell) \quad \Delta H = ?$$

Show your working clearly.

2

3. Vinaigrette salad dressing can be made using the following ingredients:

Ingredients
Olive oil
Salt
Vinegar (ethanoic acid)
Dijon mustard (emulsifier)
Water

Using your knowledge of chemistry, comment on how the ingredients present in the vinaigrette dressing will interact with each other.

3

4. X-ray diffraction is a technique used to determine the structures of molecules. The scattering intensity of an X-ray beam hitting a sample allows us to determine the shape of a molecule. An example is shown:

X-ray electron density map   Electron density map over molecule

Hydroxybenzene (phenol), C_6H_5OH

(a) The hydrogen atoms do not show up clearly on an electron density map. Suggest a reason for this.

1

(b) Shown below is an electron density map of another molecule.

Draw the full structural formula of this molecule.

1

MARKS

5. Sulfur is removed from impure blast furnace iron by the addition of magnesium powder. Magnesium sulfide is formed, which then floats on top of the molten iron and is removed.

$$Mg + S \longrightarrow MgS$$

(a) (i) **Explain fully** the difference in size between an atom of sulfur and an atom of magnesium.

2

   (ii) Write the equation for the first ionisation enthalpy of magnesium.

1

(b) Calculate the theoretical mass, in kilograms, of magnesium sulfide produced by a blast furnace if 100 kg of magnesium were added.

Show your working clearly.

2

6. An investigation into the use of metals to produce hydrogen as a fuel for cars was carried out.

10·36 g of lead was added to 50 cm³ of 1 mol l⁻¹ hydrochloric acid to generate hydrogen gas.

The balanced equation for the reaction is:

$$Pb(s) + 2HCl(aq) \longrightarrow PbCl_2(aq) + H_2(g)$$

(a) Show by calculation which reactant is in excess.

   Show your working clearly.

                                                                                        2

(b) Calculate the mass of hydrogen gas which will have been given off during the experiment.

   Show your working clearly.

                                                                                        1

(c) The hydrogen produced in the reaction can be contaminated with hydrogen chloride vapour, which is very soluble in water.

   Complete the following diagram to show how the hydrogen chloride could be removed before the hydrogen is collected.   **1**

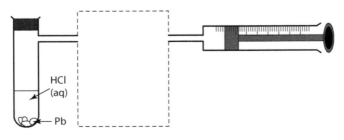

HCl (aq)

Pb

MARKS

7. The table shown compares the properties of ethanol and propane.

Hydrocarbon	Boiling point	State at room temperature	Solubility in water	Formula mass
Ethanol	78.4 °C	liquid	soluble	46
Propane	−42 °C	gas	insoluble	44

Explain fully why, although propane and ethanol have very similar formula masses, they have very different properties.

You should give mention to both the bonding and intermolecular forces involved and how they arise.

4

8. Manufacturers of scented soap products suggest that soap should be stored in cool, dry conditions when not in use to prolong the life of the soap and to maintain its scent.

    Using your knowledge of chemistry, comment on why the soap should be stored in cool, dry conditions.

3

9. Car companies are developing fuel cells as a replacement for conventional petrol and diesel engines to power their vehicles.

Initially car companies were looking at methanol fuel cells, but they found some disadvantages with those when compared to hydrogen fuel cells.

(a) The ion-electron equations for both the oxidation and the reduction reactions that take place in a methanol fuel cell are:

$$CH_3OH(\ell) + H_2O(\ell) \longrightarrow CO_2(g) + 6H^+(aq) + 6e^-$$
$$3O_2(g) + 12H^+(aq) + 12e^- \longrightarrow 6H_2O(\ell)$$

Combine the two ion-electron equations to give the equation for the overall redox reaction.

1

(b) (i) The equation for the reaction in a hydrogen fuel cell is:

$$2H_2(g) + O_2(g) \longrightarrow 2H_2O(\ell)$$

Using bond enthalpy values, calculate the enthalpy change, in kJ, for the reaction.

Show your working clearly.

2

(ii) Suggest a disadvantage of using a methanol fuel cell when compared to a hydrogen fuel cell.

1

10. Acidified potassium permanganate can be used to determine the concentration of iron(II) sulfate solution by titration.

(a) (i) A standard solution of potassium permanganate is required to perform the titration.

State what is meant by the term 'standard solution'.

1

(ii) Describe how a standard solution is prepared from a weighed sample of potassium permanganate.

2

(b) (i) An average of 8·35 cm^3 of iron(II) sulfate solution was required to completely react with 25 cm^3 of 0·2 mol l^{-1} potassium permanganate solution.

The equation for this reaction is:

$$5Fe^{2+}(aq) + MnO_4^-(aq) + 8H^+(aq) \longrightarrow 5Fe^{3+}(aq) + Mn^{2+}(aq) + 4H_2O(\ell)$$

Calculate the concentration, in mol l^{-1}, of the iron(II) sulfate solution.

Show your working clearly.

3

(continued)

    (ii) During the reaction the permanganate ion is reduced to manganese. Complete the ion–electron equation for the reduction of the permanganate ion.

$$MnO_4^-(aq) \longrightarrow Mn^{2+}(aq)$$

1

(c) The recommended daily allowance (RDA) for iron is 27 mg for pregnant women.

A breakfast cereal provides 3·6 mg of iron per 30 g of cereal.

What percentage of the RDA is provided by 100 g of this cereal?

2

Practice Papers for SQA Exams: Higher Chemistry Exam 1

MARKS

DO NOT
WRITE IN
THIS
MARGIN

11. The enthalpy of combustion of ethanol can be obtained using the apparatus shown.

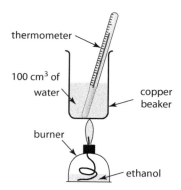

(a) In the experiment it was found that burning 0·64 g of ethanol increased the temperature of the water by 10·0 °C.

Calculate the enthalpy of combustion, in kJ mol⁻¹, of ethanol.

Show your working clearly.

3

(b) The energy density value of a fuel is the energy released when one kilogram of the fuel is completely burned.

The enthalpy of combustion of ethanol stated in the data book is −1367 kJ mol⁻¹.

Calculate the energy density value, in kJ kg⁻¹, of ethanol.

Show your working clearly.

1

MARKS

DO NOT
WRITE IN
THIS
MARGIN

12. The Born-Haber cycle is an approach to analysing the energies involved in chemical reactions. Born-Haber cycles are used primarily as a means of calculating lattice enthalpies, which cannot otherwise be measured directly. An example is shown below.

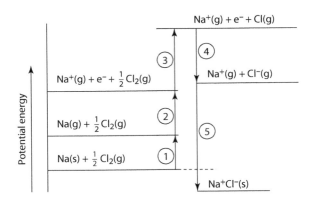

(a) Which of the five reaction stages involves the greatest release of energy?

1

(b) Write an equation for the overall reaction that is represented by this Born-Haber cycle.

1

13. Sulfuric acid is reacted with calcium carbonate to produced calcium sulfate for use in making plaster.

$$H_2SO_4(aq) + CaCO_3(s) \longrightarrow CaSO_4(aq) + CO_2(g) + H_2O(\ell)$$

(a) 490 tonnes of calcium carbonate was used to produce 550 tonnes of calcium sulfate.

Calculate the percentage yield.

Show your working clearly.

% **3**

MARKS | DO NOT WRITE IN THIS MARGIN

(continued)

(b) Calculate the atom economy for this reaction.

Show your working clearly. 2

14. Limonene is a colourless or pale yellow liquid with a sweet lemon-like odour. It occurs naturally in many essential oils, which can be used in cosmetic products.

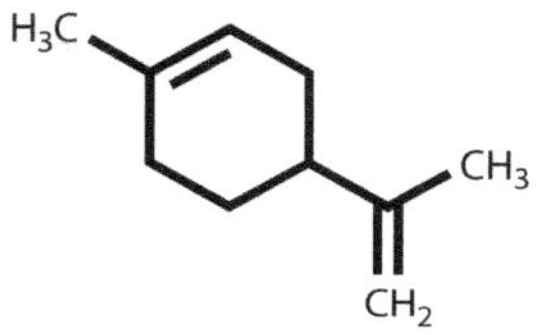

(a) To which group of compounds does limonene belong? 1

(b) Limonene can be produced by joining together isoprene units.

Give the systematic name of isoprene. 1

(c) (i) Many cosmetic products also contain free radical scavengers.

State what is meant by the term 'free radical scavengers'. 1

(ii) Free radical chain reactions involve three steps.

State the names of the three steps. 1

15. The enzyme catalase increases the rate of the decomposition of hydrogen peroxide.

The equation for this reaction is:

$$2H_2O_2(aq) \longrightarrow 2H_2O(\ell) + O_2(g)$$

The results obtained are presented in the graph shown.

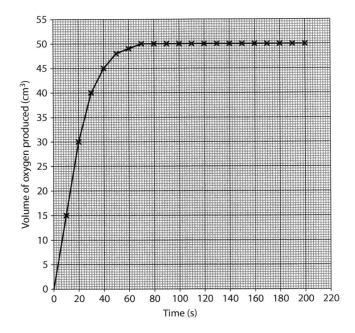

(a) Calculate the rate of the reaction, in s^{-1}, at 40 seconds.

1

(b) Enzymes are biological catalysts.

State the name of the functional group found in all enzymes.

1

(continued)

(c) Draw a labelled diagram of the assembled apparatus that could be used to perform this experiment in the lab.

2

16. Ketones, such as heptan-2-one, are responsible for the smell associated with blue cheese. These ketones are only found in the cheese after a ripening process has been undertaken.

(a) Name the functional group present in heptan-2-one.

1

(b) Name the alcohol that can be oxidised to produce heptan-2-one.

1

(c) Proteins in milk are broken down first into peptides, then amino acids, and finally converted into a range of other molecules contributing to the taste and smell of the cheese.

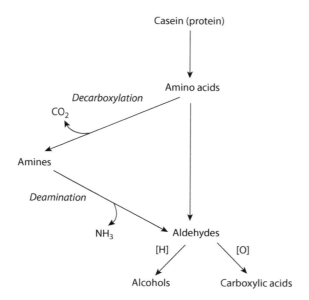

(continued)

(i) Name the reaction that turns proteins into amino acids.

1

(ii) Decarboxylation turns amino acids into amines, which are compounds that only contain an amino group.

Draw the structure of the amine produced on decarboxylation of the amino acid glycine.

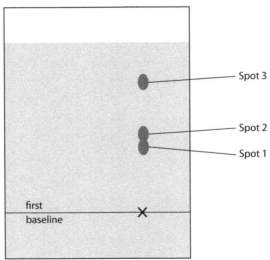

1

(d) The mixtures of amino acids produced were separated using paper chromatography.

The retention factor, Rf, for a substance can be calculated using the equation

$$Rf = \frac{\text{distance moved by the substance}}{\text{maximum distance moved by the solvent}}$$

MARKS

DO NOT
WRITE IN
THIS
MARGIN

Practice Papers for SQA Exams: Higher Chemistry Exam 1

(continued)

(i) Which of the spots would have the highest Rf value?

1

(ii) **Explain** why different amino acids travel different distances up the chromatography paper.

1

17. Nitrogen dioxide can be produced in different ways.

(a) Industrially, it can be prepared as part of the Ostwald Process. The process involves passing ammonia and oxygen gases over a hot platinum catalyst to produce nitrogen monoxide, which is then oxidised to produce nitrogen dioxide.

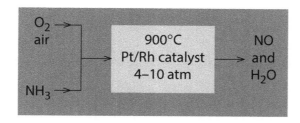

Suggest why the platinum catalyst is used as fine wire gauze.

1

(b) The equation for the reaction taking place is:

$$4NH_3(g) + 5O_2 \rightleftharpoons 4NO(g) + 6H_2O(g) \qquad \Delta H = -909 \text{ kJ mol}^{-1}$$

(i) Give two reasons why this process is profitable.

2

(ii) **Explain fully** why a low pressure is used in this process.

2

(iii) Any equilibrium can be described in terms of its equilibrium constant, K.

For the following reaction at equilibrium,

$$wA + xB \longrightarrow yC + zD$$

The equilibrium constant is given by:

$$K = \frac{[C]^y[D]^z}{[A]^w[B]^x}$$

Use this information to complete the equation for the equilibrium constant for the production of nitrogen monoxide.

2

(iv) Nitrogen dioxide can also be prepared by heating copper(II) nitrate.

$$Cu(NO_3)_2(s) \longrightarrow CuO_{(s)} + 2NO_2(g) + \tfrac{1}{2}O_2(g)$$

Calculate the volume of nitrogen dioxide produced when 4·0 g of copper(II) nitrate is completely decomposed on heating.

(Take the molar volume of nitrogen dioxide to be 24 litres mol^{-1}.)

Show your working clearly.

3

SECTION 1 ANSWER GRID

Mark the correct answer as shown

	A	B	C	D
1	○	○	○	○
2	○	○	○	○
3	○	○	○	○
4	○	○	○	○
5	○	○	○	○
6	○	○	○	○
7	○	○	○	○
8	○	○	○	○
9	○	○	○	○
10	○	○	○	○
11	○	○	○	○
12	○	○	○	○
13	○	○	○	○
14	○	○	○	○
15	○	○	○	○
16	○	○	○	○
17	○	○	○	○
18	○	○	○	○
19	○	○	○	○
20	○	○	○	○

Practice Exam 2

CfE Higher Chemistry

Practice Papers for SQA Exams

Exam 2

Fill in these boxes and read what is printed below.

Full name of centre

Town

Forename(s)

Surname

Try to answer all of the questions in the time allowed.

Total marks – 100

Section 1 – 20 marks

Section 2 – 80 marks

Read all questions carefully before attempting.

You have 2 hours to complete this paper.

Write your answers in the spaces provided, including all of your working.

Scotland's leading educational publishers

SECTION 1 – 20 marks

Attempt ALL questions

Answers should be given on the separate answer sheet provided.

1. Which of the following chlorides has the **most** ionic character?

    A NaCl

    B CsCl

    C $CaCl_2$

    D $AlCl_3$

2. The potential energy diagram shown refers to a reversible reaction.

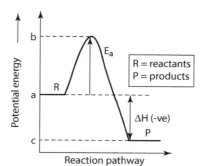

    What is the activation energy, E_a, expressed in terms of a, b, c for the **reverse** reaction?

    A $E_a = b - a$

    B $E_a = b + a$

    C $E_a = b - c$

    D $E_a = b + c$

3. A small increase in the temperature of a reaction mixture results in a large increase in the reaction rate. The main reason for this is

    A the activation energy is lowered

    B the enthalpy change is increased

    C the enthalpy change is decreased

    D the kinetic energy of the particles is increased.

4. The element francium occurs in Group 1 of the periodic table. Of all the elements in Group 1, francium will have the

A highest first ionisation energy

B lowest electronegativity

C smallest covalent radius

D lowest relative atomic mass.

5. An unknown element is found to have a melting point of over 2000 °C, but an oxide of this element is a gas at room temperature.

Which of the following types of bonding is most likely to be present in the element?

A Metallic

B Pure covalent

C Ionic

D Polar covalent

6. Which of the following compounds has polar molecules?

A

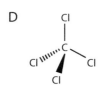

B

C $O\!=\!\!=\!C\!=\!\!=\!O$

D

7. Which of the following elements would require the **most** energy to convert one mole of gaseous atoms into one mole of gaseous ions carrying a two positive charge?

    A Iron

    B Cobalt

    C Nickel

    D Copper

8. Which of the following compounds is a ketone?

    A

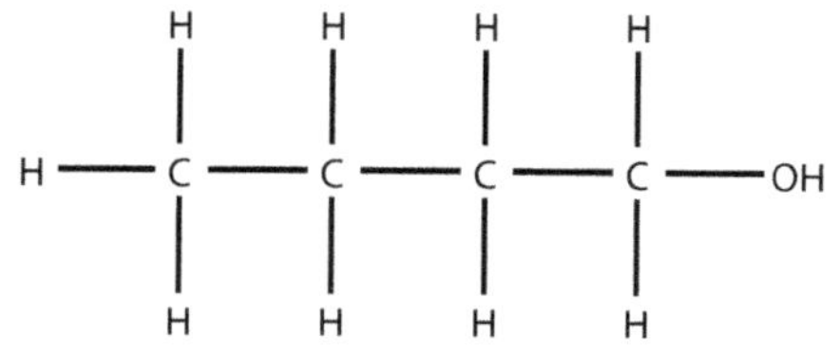

    B

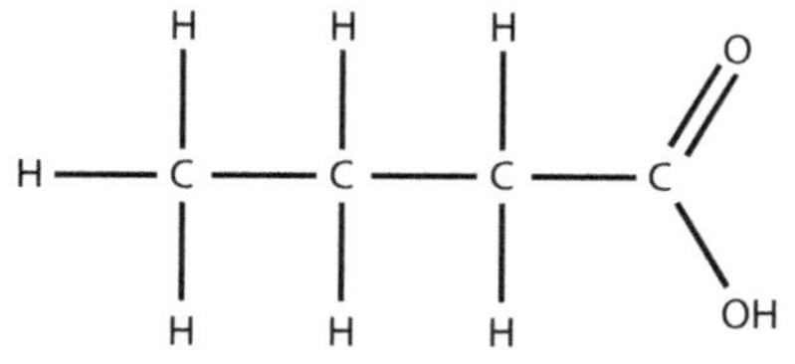

    C

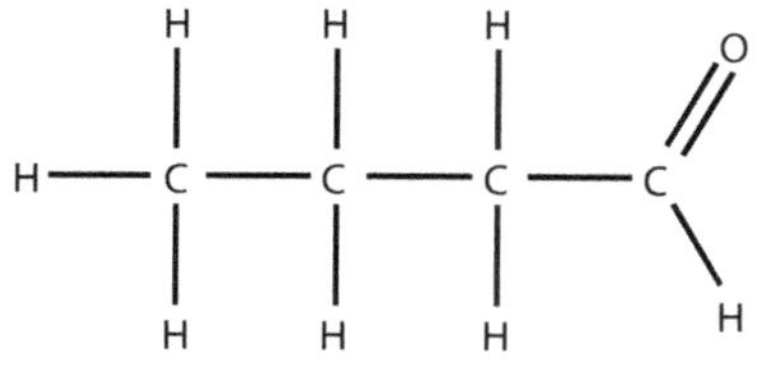

    D

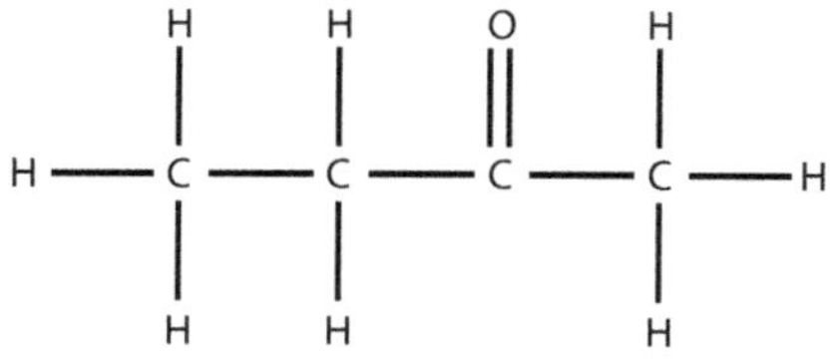

9. Glycerol is a chemical compound also commonly called glycerin or glycerine. Which of the following is the correct systematic name for glycerol?

    A Propan-2-ol

    B Propane-1,2,3-triol

    C Propanoic acid

    D Propyl propanoate

10. Fats have a higher melting point than oils because, compared to oils, fats

    A have a higher degree of unsaturation

    B have more loosely packed molecules

    C have fewer carbon atoms

    D have a higher degree of saturation.

11. Which of the following is an isomer of hexanal?

    A 3-methylpentan-2-one

    B 2,2-dimethylbutan-1-ol

    C 2-methylbutanal

    D 3-ethylpentanal

12. Amino acids are converted into proteins by

    A addition

    B hydrolysis

    C esterification

    D condensation.

13. Which of the following could be prepared by reacting a secondary alcohol with acidified potassium dichromate solution?

    A $H-\underset{\parallel}{\overset{}{C}}-H$ with $=O$ (structure: H–C(=O)–H)

    B $CH_3-\underset{\parallel}{\overset{}{C}}-CH_3$ with $=O$ (structure: CH₃–C(=O)–CH₃)

    C $KO-\underset{\parallel}{\overset{}{C}}-CH_3$ with $=O$ (structure: KO–C(=O)–CH₃)

    D $CH_3-O-\underset{\parallel}{\overset{}{C}}-CH_3$ with $=O$ (structure: CH₃–O–C(=O)–CH₃)

14. In a reversible reaction, equilibrium is established when

A the concentration of the reactants and products is equal

B the concentration of the reactants and products is constant

C the concentration of only the products remains unchanged

D the concentration of only the reactants remains unchanged.

15. In which of the following reactions would a change in pressure **not** affect the yield of product?

A $ICl(\ell) + Cl_2(g) \rightleftharpoons ICl_3(s)$

B $2NO_2(g) \rightleftharpoons N_2O_4(g)$

C $H_2(g) + I_2(g) \rightleftharpoons 2HI(g)$

D $N_2(g) + 3H_2(g) \rightleftharpoons 2NH_3(g)$

16. Stannic chloride ($SnCl_4$) was used in World War I as a chemical weapon due to its corrosive and toxic properties. It can be produced by the reaction shown.

$HgCl_2 + SnCl_2 \longrightarrow Hg + SnCl_4$

Which of the following ions is oxidised in the above reaction?

A Sn^{2+}

B Sn^{4+}

C Hg^{2+}

D Cl^-

17. The equation for the complete combustion of methane is shown below.

$CH_4(g) + 2O_2(g) \longrightarrow CO_2(g) + 2H_2O(\ell)$

If 20 cm³ of methane is ignited and burned with 100 cm³ of oxygen, what is the volume of the resulting gas mixture?

A 20 cm³

B 50 cm³

C 80 cm³

D 120 cm³

18. State the enthalpy of formation of carbon monoxide (reaction X) using the reaction pathway shown.

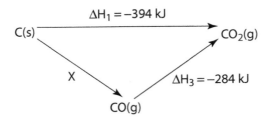

A −110 kJ mol^{-1}

B +110 kJ mol^{-1}

C −678 kJ mol^{-1}

D +678 kJ mol^{-1}

19. Some bond enthalpies are shown below.

Bond	Enthalpy/kJ mol^{-1}
H–H	436
C–C	348
C–H	412
C=C	612

Use the information in the table to calculate the enthalpy change for the following reaction.

$$\underset{H}{\overset{H}{>}}C = C\underset{H}{\overset{H}{<}} \;+\; H-H \;\longrightarrow\; H-\underset{\underset{H}{|}}{\overset{\overset{H}{|}}{C}}-\underset{\underset{H}{|}}{\overset{\overset{H}{|}}{C}}-H$$

A −124 kJ

B +124 kJ

C −274 kJ

D +274 kJ

20. In chromatography, the identity of a component can be indicated either by the distance it has travelled or by the time it has taken to travel through the apparatus. The time taken is called the

A reaction time

B relation time

C resultant time

D retention time.

SECTION 2 – 80 marks

Attempt ALL questions

1. Shown below is part of a protein molecule.

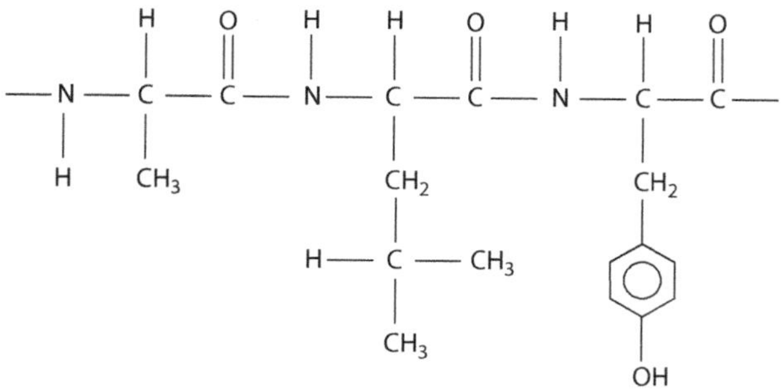

(a) Circle a peptide link in the structure.

1

(b) Draw the structural formula for one of the amino acid molecules that would be formed if this protein were hydrolysed.

1

(c) Some amino acids are known as essential amino acids.

State what is meant by the term essential amino acid.

1

2. Patterns in electronegativity, covalent radius and ionisation enthalpy can all be found in the periodic table.

(a) State what is meant by the term electronegativity.

1

(b) **Explain fully** why electronegativity decreases going down a group in the periodic table.

2

(c) **Explain fully** the trend in covalent radius going across the periodic table from potassium to krypton.

2

(d) **Explain fully** why the first ionisation enthalpy of sodium is less than the first ionisation enthalpy of lithium.

2

3. The effect of changing the temperature on the rate of a reaction can be studied using the following reaction.

$$5(COOH)_2(aq) + 6H^+(aq) + 2MnO_4^-(aq) \longrightarrow 2Mn^{2+}(aq) + 10CO_2(g) + 8H_2O(\ell)$$

(a) Draw a diagram to illustrate how the rate of this reaction could be monitored in the lab.

2

(b) **Explain fully** why increasing the temperature results in an increase in the rate of a chemical reaction.

2

(c) The graph shown illustrates the kinetic energy for molecules at a certain temperature.

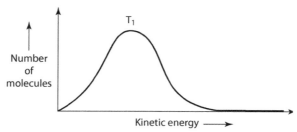

Draw a new line on the graph that you would expect to see if the temperature were increased.

1

4. Citric acid is a preservative which occurs naturally in citrus fruits and can also be added to food and drinks to give an acidic or sour taste.

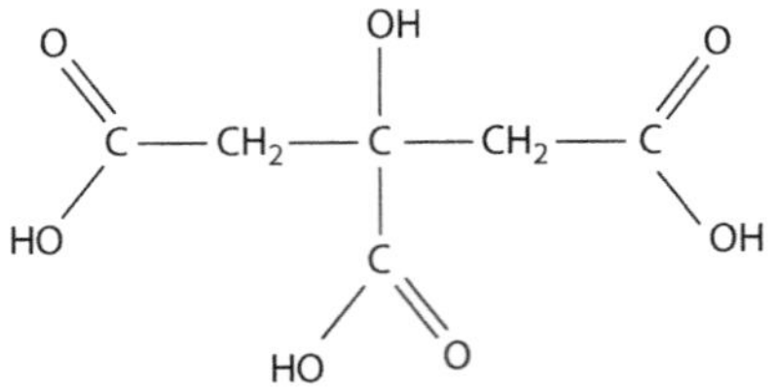

(a) **Explain fully**, with reference to the structure of citric acid, why it is very soluble in water.

2

(b) Citrus fruits also contain esters, which are partly responsible for the flavour of the fruit.

The ester shown is found in pineapples.

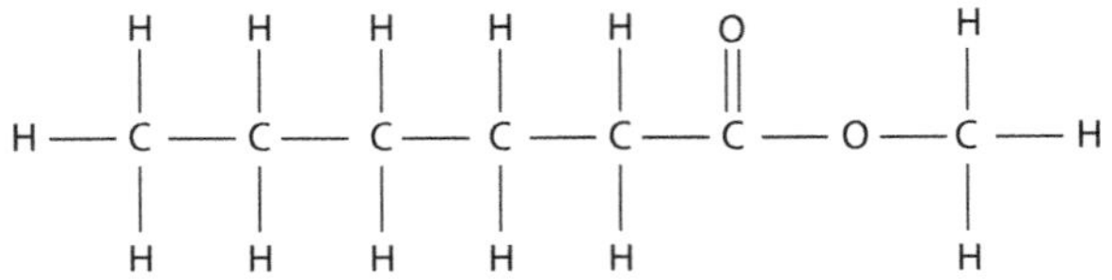

(i) Give the name of the ester.

1

(ii) A student produced this ester in the lab and obtained a yield of 65 %.

Calculate the mass of the ester (formula mass 130 g) the student produced if they reacted 22·2 g of alcohol (formula mass 32 g).

Show your working clearly.

3

5. Carbon monoxide is a tasteless, colourless but highly toxic gas and yet despite this it was once used as a domestic fuel.

One method of production of carbon monoxide involves calcium carbonate.

$$Zn + CaCO_3 \longrightarrow ZnO + CaO + CO$$

(a) Write the ion–electron equation for the oxidation step in the reaction.

1

(b) Calculate the atom economy for the formation of carbon monoxide in this reaction.

Show your working clearly.

2

(c) Carbon monoxide can also be produced in the lab as a product of the reaction of carbon dioxide with hot carbon.

The carbon dioxide is made by the reaction of dilute hydrochloric acid with solid calcium carbonate. Unreacted carbon dioxide is removed before the carbon monoxide is collected by displacement of water.

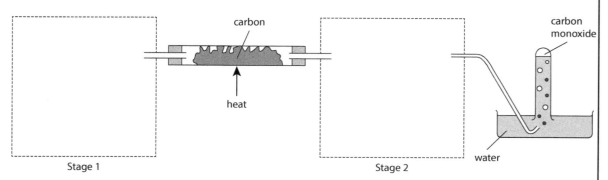

Complete the diagram showing how the carbon dioxide is produced in stage 1 and how the excess carbon dioxide is removed using limewater in stage 2.

2

6. Alkynes are a family of hydrocarbons that contain a carbon-to-carbon triple bond in their structures.

The first member of the alkynes is ethyne, which has the formula C_2H_2.

(a) Due to their functional group, alkynes can undergo addition reactions, which involve the addition of a diatomic molecule across a triple or double bond.

One example is shown:

$$H-C\equiv C-H \xrightarrow{\text{HCl}} \text{Compound X} \xrightarrow{\text{HCl}} \text{Compound Y}$$

Draw a possible full structural formula for compounds X and Y.

2

(b) Ethanol can also be produced from ethyne by an addition reaction with water. The ethanol produced can undergo oxidation.

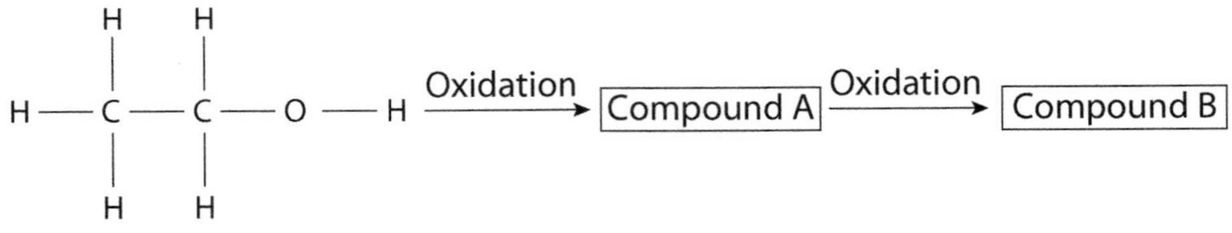

$$\xrightarrow{\text{Oxidation}} \boxed{\text{Compound A}} \xrightarrow{\text{Oxidation}} \boxed{\text{Compound B}}$$

Name compounds A and B.

2

(continued)

(c) The equation for the enthalpy of formation of ethyne is:

$$2C(s) + H_2(g) \longrightarrow C_2H_2(g)$$

Use the enthalpies of combustion of ethyne, carbon and hydrogen given below to calculate the enthalpy of formation of ethyne.

$$C_2H_2(g) + 2\tfrac{1}{2}O_2(g) \longrightarrow 2CO_2(g) + H_2O(\ell) \qquad \Delta H = -1301 \text{ kJ mol}^{-1}$$

$$C(s) + O_2(g) \longrightarrow CO_2(g) \qquad \Delta H = -394 \text{ kJ mol}^{-1}$$

$$H_2(s) + \tfrac{1}{2}O_2(g) \longrightarrow H_2O(\ell) \qquad \Delta H = -286 \text{ kJ mol}^{-1}$$

Show your working clearly.

2

7. The properties of four different substances are shown in the table.

Substance	Melting point (°C)	Boiling point (°C)
A	−77	−33
B	1414	3265
C	405	482
D	660	2519

(a) Complete the table below by using the letters to show the type of bonding and structure present in each substance.

Substance	Bonding and structure
	Metallic
	Ionic
	Covalent molecular
	Covalent network

2

(continued)

(b) Ethane has a boiling point of –89 °C, however methanol has a boiling point of 65 °C.

Explain fully why methanol has a high boiling point relative to methane. 3

8. Hydrogenation results in the conversion of liquid vegetable oils to solid or semi-solid fats, such as those present in margarine.

(a) **Explain fully** why fats have a higher melting point than oils. 2

(b) What is the main class of organic compound found in fats and oils? 1

(continued)

(c) The best-selling margarine contains 0·1 g of sodium per 10 g of margarine. The sodium is present in the margarine as sodium chloride.

Calculate the mass of sodium chloride, in g, present in a 500 g tub of margarine.

Show your working clearly.

2

9. Scottish scientist Sir William Ramsay is credited with the discovery of the noble gases. The final two noble gases he discovered, through the distillation of air, were krypton and xenon. The names he gave to these new elements were derived from the Greek words 'kryptos' meaning hidden and 'xenos' meaning stranger.

Using your knowledge of chemistry, comment on the discovery of the noble gases and the names chosen by Ramsay.

3

10. Hydrogen peroxide is used medically as an antiseptic for cleaning wounds. The concentration of a hydrogen peroxide solution can be calculated by titration with acidified potassium permanganate.

The reaction is represented by the equation:

$$2MnO_4^-(aq) + 6H^+(aq) + 5H_2O_2(aq) \longrightarrow 2Mn^{2+}(aq) + 8H_2O(\ell) + 5O_2(g)$$

25 cm³ of hydrogen peroxide was titrated with a 0.1 mol l⁻¹ acidified potassium permanganate solution and the results are shown in the table.

Titration	Volume of potassium permanganate/cm³
1	16·2
2	15·7
3	15·9

(a) (i) Suggest why the potassium permanganate solution is acidified.

1

(ii) Suggest why no indicator is required in this titration.

1

(b) Use the results shown in the table to calculate the concentration, in mol l⁻¹, of the hydrogen peroxide solution.

Show your working clearly.

3

MARKS

11. Household drains are most commonly blocked by grease, fat, soap and protein deposits such as hair.

One of the most common substances used to unblock drains is a solution of caustic soda (sodium hydroxide), which can break down these substances.

Using your knowledge of chemistry, comment on the reactions that may be taking place as the caustic soda reacts with the blockages.

3

12. Synthesis gas is a mixture of hydrogen and carbon monoxide and can be prepared as shown below.

Nickel is known to catalyse the reaction.

$$CH_4(g) + H_2O(g) \rightleftharpoons 3H_2(g) + CO(g)$$

(a) (i) An increase in temperature increases the yield of synthesis gas.

State the type of enthalpy change for the forward reaction.

1

(continued)

(ii) **Explain fully** how a change in pressure will affect the composition of the equilibrium mixture.

2

(iii) State how the composition of the equilibrium mixture would be affected by the use of the catalyst.

1

(b) A reaction sequence involving an addition reaction between synthesis gas and propene is shown:

$$2H_2(g) + 2CO(g) + 2C_3H_6(g) \longrightarrow CH_3CH_2CH_2CHO(\ell) + \text{ compound B}$$
compound A

compound A $\longrightarrow$ butan-1-ol

compound B $\longrightarrow$ alkanol C

Compound A and compound B are isomers of different types of organic compound.

(i) Name the type of organic compounds to which compound B belongs.

1

(ii) Draw the full structural formula of compound B and name it.

2

MARKS

DO NOT
WRITE IN
THIS
MARGIN

(continued)   Practice Papers for SQA Exams: Higher Chemistry Exam 2

(iii) If pentan-1-ol were required as a product instead of butan-1-ol, which reagent would be used instead of propene?

1

(c) (i) Name the type of chemical reaction which would occur if hexan-1-ol reacted with ethanoic acid.

1

(ii) Draw the full structural formula for the product of this reaction.

1

(iii) Give a possible use of this product.

1

MARKS

DO NOT
WRITE IN
THIS
MARGIN

Practice Papers for SQA Exams: Higher Chemistry Exam 2

13. White tin has metallic properties but at temperatures below 13 °C it changes slowly to grey tin, in which each atom is joined covalently to four others.

When heated in air, tin forms tin(IV) oxide, SnO_2. Heated tin also reacts with chlorine to form tin(IV) chloride, $SnCl_4$, a colourless liquid (b.p. 114 °C).

(a) State the type of bonding in tin(IV) chloride.

1

(b) The main source of tin is the ore cassiterite or tinstone, SnO_2. After preliminary treatment the concentrated ore is heated in a furnace with coke at about 1200 °C.

$$SnO_2(s) + C(s) \longrightarrow Sn(s) + CO_2(g)$$

(i) Name the reducing agent in this reaction.

1

(ii) Calculate the volume of carbon dioxide produced in this reaction if 500 g of cassiterite is completely converted to tin.

Take the molar volume to be 24 litres mol^{-1}

Show your working clearly.

3

MARKS

14. The crystal structure of an ionic compound is determined by the 'radius ratio' of the ions involved.

$$\text{Radius ratio} = \frac{\text{Ionic radius of positive ion}}{\text{Ionic radius of negative ion}}$$

Explain clearly, showing your working, why magnesium oxide is likely to have the same crystal structure as sodium chloride. (You may use your data booklet to help you.)

2

15. The diagram below shows the energy changes for the reaction

A+B $\longrightarrow$ C+D

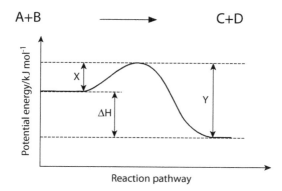

(a) (i) Using the symbols X and Y from the diagram, construct a simple equation to show how the enthalpy change for the forward reaction could be calculated.

1

(ii) State how the values of X and Y could be decreased with no change in ΔH.

1

(b) Suggest why some collisions of particles A and B result in no reaction.

1

(c) For the reaction

$$2HI \longrightarrow H_2 + I_2$$

draw a structural diagram to represent a possible activated complex.

1

16. The chlorine atoms in chlorofluorocarbons destroy ozone, O_3, in the upper atmosphere.

There are three main steps in this process.

Step 1   The chlorofluorocarbons are broken down to form free radicals.

$$CCl_3F \rightarrow \cdot CCl_2F + \cdot Cl$$

Step 2   Chlorine radicals react with ozone molecules, breaking them down into oxygen molecules.

Step 3   The reactions in step 2 regenerate the chlorine radicals, so they can go on to destroy more ozone molecules.

(a) Give the names of the three mains steps in this free radical process.

1

(b) State what provides the energy to break the bonds in chlorofluorocarbons in the upper atmosphere.

1

(c) State what is meant by the term 'free radical'.

1

(d) Write a possible equation for step 2.

1

(e) What is added to cosmetics to prevent similar chain reactions taking place on the skin?

1

SECTION 1 ANSWER GRID

Mark the correct answer as shown

	A	B	C	D
1	○	○	○	○
2	○	○	○	○
3	○	○	○	○
4	○	○	○	○
5	○	○	○	○
6	○	○	○	○
7	○	○	○	○
8	○	○	○	○
9	○	○	○	○
10	○	○	○	○
11	○	○	○	○
12	○	○	○	○
13	○	○	○	○
14	○	○	○	○
15	○	○	○	○
16	○	○	○	○
17	○	○	○	○
18	○	○	○	○
19	○	○	○	○
20	○	○	○	○

Practice Exam 3

CfE Higher Chemistry

Practice Papers for SQA Exams

Exam 3

Fill in these boxes and read what is printed below.

Full name of centre

Town

Forename(s)

Surname

Try to answer all of the questions in the time allowed.

Total marks – 100

Section 1 – 20 marks

Section 2 – 80 marks

Read all questions carefully before attempting.

You have 2 hours to complete this paper.

Write your answers in the spaces provided, including all of your working.

Leckie×Leckie

Scotland's leading educational publishers

SECTION 1 – 20 marks

Attempt ALL questions

Answers should be given on the separate answer sheet provided.

1. The potential energy diagram for a reaction is shown.

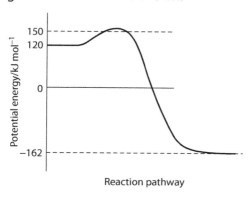

The enthalpy change for the forward reaction, in kJ mol^{-1}, is

A −42

B 155

C −282

D −182.

2.

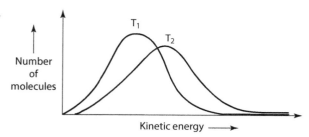

Which line in the table correctly interprets the above energy distribution diagram as the temperature increases from T_1 to T_2?

	Activation energy (E_a)	Number of successful collisions
A	Unchanged	Increases
B	Unchanged	Decreases
C	Increases	Increases
D	Increases	Decreases

3. What type of bond is broken when ice is melted?

A Covalent

B Polar covalent

C London dispersion

D Hydrogen

4. Which of the following elements is the least electronegative?

A Fluorine

B Chlorine

C Sodium

D Caesium

5. Which of the following reactions represents the first ionisation energy of chlorine?

A $Cl_2(\ell) + e^-$ ⟶ $Cl^-(g)$

B $Cl_2(g) + 2e^-$ ⟶ $2Cl^-(g)$

C $Cl(g)$ ⟶ $Cl^+(g) + e^-$

D $Cl(g)$ ⟶ $Cl^{2+}(g) + 2e^-$

6. The difference between the covalent radius of sodium and chlorine is mainly due to the difference in the

A number of energy levels

B number of neutrons

C number of protons

D mass of each atom.

7. Which of the following has a covalent molecular structure?

A Argon

B Fullerene

C Calcium chloride

D Graphite

8. Three moles of oxygen is mixed with one mole of methane gas and ignited.

$$CH_4(g) + 2O_2(g) \longrightarrow CO_2(g) + 2H_2O(\ell)$$

Which is the correct number of moles of gas in the resulting gas mixture at room temperature?

A 1

B 2

C 3

D 4

9. Which of the following is an isomer of 3,3-dimethylbutan-1-ol?

A $CH_3CH_2CH(CH_3)CH_2OH$

B $CH_3CH(CH_3)CH(CH_3)CH_2OH$

C $CH_3CH_2CH(CH_3)CH_2OH$

D $CH_3CH(CH_3)C(CH_3)_2CH_2OH$

10. Paracetamol is a widely used over-the-counter pain reliever.

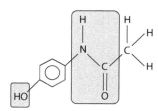

Which two functional groups are highlighted in the structure of paracetamol?

A Amide link and hydroxyl

B Hydroxyl and carbonyl

C Amine and carbonyl

D Amine and carboxyl

11. Which of the following would not react with acidified potassium dichromate solution?

A Butan-2-ol

B Butanone

C Methanol

D Methanal

12. The compound shown is an example of

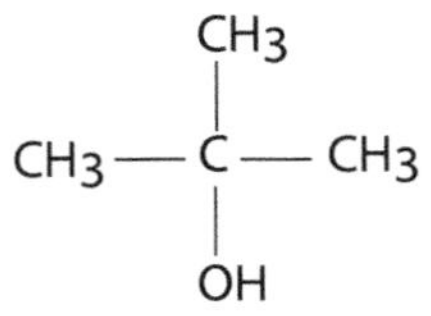

$$CH_3 - \overset{\overset{\displaystyle CH_3}{|}}{\underset{\underset{\displaystyle OH}{|}}{C}} - CH_3$$

A a primary alcohol

B a secondary alcohol

C a tertiary alcohol

D an aldehyde.

13. Pineapple flavouring is based on the compound shown.

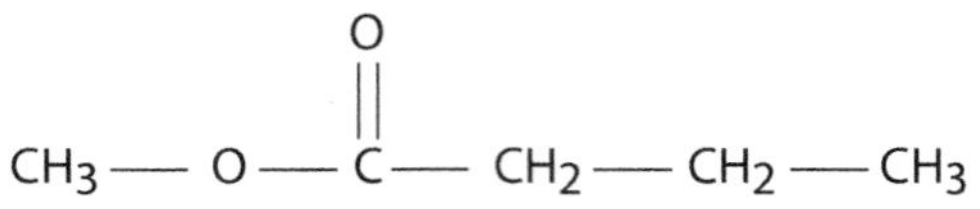

$$CH_3 - O - \overset{\overset{\displaystyle O}{||}}{C} - CH_2 - CH_2 - CH_3$$

It can be produced from

A methanol and butanoic acid

B propanol and ethanoic acid

C butanol and methanoic acid

D propanol and propanoic acid.

14. When an egg is heated the protein it contains is denatured, causing it to change colour from colourless to white.

During denaturing, the protein molecule

A is oxidised

B is hydrolysed

C is reduced

D changes shape.

15. Glycerol contains

    A no hydroxyl groups

    B 1 hydroxyl group

    C 2 hydroxyl groups

    D 3 hydroxyl groups.

16. The three equations shown below all involve displacement reactions between metals and metal oxides.

$$Mg(s) + FeO(s) \longrightarrow MgO(s) + Fe(s) \quad \Delta H = \mathbf{A} \text{ kJ mol}^{-1}$$

$$Fe(s) + CuO(s) \longrightarrow FeO(s) + Cu(s) \quad \Delta H = \mathbf{B} \text{ kJ mol}^{-1}$$

$$Mg(s) + CuO(s) \longrightarrow MgO(s) + Cu(s) \quad \Delta H = \mathbf{C} \text{ kJ mol}^{-1}$$

Which is the correct relationship between A, B and C according to Hess's Law?

    A $A + B = -C$

    B $A + B = C$

    C $C + A = -B$

    D $C + A = B$

17. The enthalpy of combustion is always the energy released when

    A 1 mole of a substance is completely burned in excess oxygen

    B an excess of substance is burned in 1 mole of oxygen

    C 1 g of a substance is completely burned in excess oxygen

    D an excess of substance is burned in 1 g of oxygen.

18. One method used to produce methanol requires synthesis gas. The following equation shows the production of methanol from synthesis gas.

$$2H_2(g) + CO(g) \quad \rightleftharpoons \quad CH_3OH(g) \qquad \Delta H = -91\,kJ\,mol^{-1}$$

Which line in the table shows the conditions that would cause the greatest increase in the amount of methanol produced?

	Pressure	Temperature
A	High	High
B	Low	Low
C	High	Low
D	Low	High

19. Potassium chlorate can undergo thermal decomposition to produce potassium chloride and oxygen gas.

$$2KClO_3(s) \longrightarrow 2KCl(s) + 3O_2(g)$$

What volume of oxygen would be obtained by the decomposition of 0.05 moles of potassium chlorate in such a reaction?

(The molar volume of oxygen under these conditions is 24 litres mol^{-1}.)

A 0·15 litres

B 0·3 litres

C 1·8 litres

D 3·6 litres

20. A solution of accurately known concentration is more commonly known as a

A correct solution

B precise solution

C prepared solution

D standard solution.

MARKS

SECTION 2 – 80 marks

Attempt ALL questions

1. Phenylalanine is an essential amino acid, which is found naturally in the breast milk of mammals.

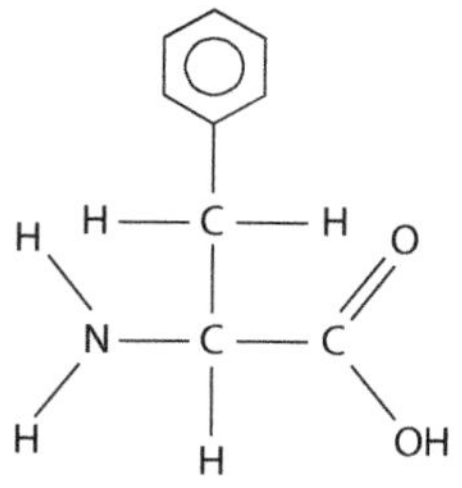

   (a) State what is meant by the term 'essential amino acid'.

1

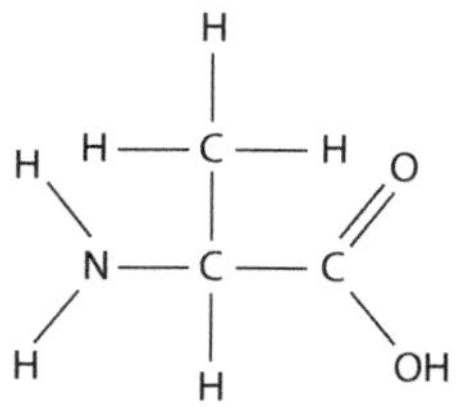

alanine

   (b) Alanine, another amino acid, can combine with phenylalanine to form a dipeptide. Draw a possible full structural formula of the molecule formed when one molecule of alanine joins with one molecule of phenylalanine.

1

(continued)

(c) What name is given to the link in protein molecules that holds the amino acid molecules together?

1

(d) Proteins can be denatured by heat.

State what is meant by the term denatured.

1

(e) Proteins called enzymes can be used to catalyse the breakdown of hydrogen peroxide into water and oxygen as shown by the following equation:

$$2H_2O_2(aq) \longrightarrow 2H_2O(\ell) + O_2(g)$$

The bond enthalpy of an oxygen-to-oxygen single bond is 142 kJ mol^{-1}. Use this information and the bond enthalpy values given in the data booklet to calculate the enthalpy change, in kJ, for the reaction.

Show your working clearly.

3

MARKS

DO NOT
WRITE IN
THIS
MARGIN

Practice Papers for SQA Exams: Higher Chemistry Exam 3

2. 'When I was 9 years old, my parents gave me a chemistry set. Within a week, I had decided to become a chemist and never wavered from that choice', recalled Robert F. Curl, Jr in his Nobel Prize autobiography. Curl Jr was awarded the Nobel Prize in Chemistry in 1996 for the discovery of fullerenes, and was one of the many Nobel Prize winners who credits the kits for inspiring their career.

(a) Complete the table to show the various bonding and structures of the two forms of carbon.

Form of carbon	Bonding	Structure at room temperature
Fullerenes		
Diamond		

1

(b) Sales of chemistry sets have increased in recent years. The chemistry set shown is designed for use on typical foods found in the home.

> Chemistry of Food Experiment Kit
> 6 large test tubes
> Test tube rack
> Biuret reagent (protein indicator)
> Benedict's solution (glucose indicator)
> Lugol's iodine (starch indicator)
> Indophenol (vitamin C indicator)
> Ascorbic acid (vitamin C)
> Copper(II) oxide
> Pipette (droppers)
> 250 ml glass beaker
> Experiment guide with charts to record test results

Using your knowledge of chemistry, suggest some experiments and expected results that may be included in the experiment guide.

3

3. The structure of a fat molecule is shown.

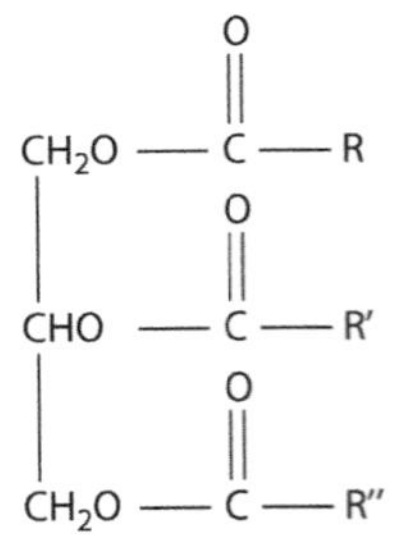

$$
\begin{array}{c}
\text{CH}_2\text{O} \longrightarrow \overset{\displaystyle \overset{O}{\|}}{C} \longrightarrow R \\
\text{CHO} \longrightarrow \overset{\displaystyle \overset{O}{\|}}{C} \longrightarrow R' \\
\text{CH}_2\text{O} \longrightarrow \overset{\displaystyle \overset{O}{\|}}{C} \longrightarrow R''
\end{array}
$$

(a) (i) When the fat is broken down, fatty acids are obtained.

The fatty acids are represented by R, R' and R'' in the diagram. Name the other product of this reaction.

1

(ii) Name the type of reaction that breaks down fats into fatty acids.

1

(b) Fats are solid at room temperature, but oils are liquid.

Explain fully why fats have a higher melting point than oils.

2

(c) State the type of compound that fats and oils can be classified as.

1

4. The potential energy diagram for a reaction is shown.

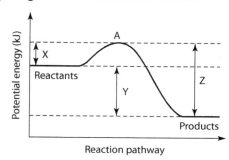

(a) State what could be used to lower the values of X and Z but would have no effect on Y.

1

(b) At point A an unstable arrangement of atoms is formed.

State the name given to this arrangement.

1

(c) State whether the value of the enthalpy change for this reaction would be positive or negative.

1

(d) Potential energy diagrams can be used to calculate the activation energy for a reaction.

Explain fully what is meant by the term activation energy.

2

5. The enthalpy of combustion of ethanol can be measured using a bomb calorimeter like the one shown.

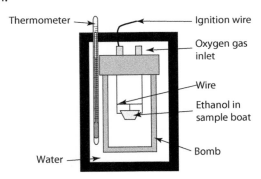

(a) The result obtained for the enthalpy of combustion of ethanol using the bomb calorimeter is higher than those obtained in the school lab.

Suggest a reason for this.

1

(b) When the experiment was performed in the calorimeter it was found that 0·92 g of ethanol resulted in the temperature of 400 cm³ of water increasing from 18·2 °C to 34·3 °C.

Calculate the enthalpy of combustion of ethanol.

Show your working clearly.

3

MARKS

DO NOT
WRITE IN
THIS
MARGIN

Practice Papers for SQA Exams: Higher Chemistry Exam 3

6. Green salt (uranium tetrafluoride) is used to produce fuel for nuclear power stations. It is produced from uranium ore.

Uranium can be extracted from green salt in a redox reaction with magnesium metal:

$$2Mg + UF_4 \longrightarrow 2MgF_2 + U$$

(a) Name the oxidising agent in this reaction.

1

(b) For this reaction to take place the UF_4 must be in the molten state. Therefore, the reaction is carried out at a temperature of over 1100 °C in an argon atmosphere.

Suggest why the reaction is not carried out in air.

1

(c) Uranium hexafluoride can also be used as a fuel for nuclear power plants. Listed below are some of the properties of UF_6.

Suggest the type of bonding in, and structure of, uranium hexafluoride.

Properties of UF_6	
Appearance	Colourless solid
Density	5·09 g cm^{-3}
Melting point	64·8°C
Hazard	Very toxic

2

MARKS

DO NOT
WRITE IN
THIS
MARGIN

Practice Papers for SQA Exams: Higher Chemistry Exam 3

7. The reaction between hydrochloric acid and magnesium can be used to calculate the molar volume of hydrogen.

$$Mg(s) + 2HCl(aq) \longrightarrow MgCl_2(aq) + H_2(g)$$

A student performed this experiment by reacting 0·20 g of magnesium with excess hydrochloric acid. The hydrogen gas was collected using the downward displacement of water into a measuring cylinder.

(a) Draw a diagram of how this experiment could be performed in the lab.

2

(b) When the reaction was complete the student had collected 200 cm³ of hydrogen gas in the measuring cylinder.

Calculate the molar volume of hydrogen gas at this temperature and pressure.

Show your working clearly.

3

(c) The student ensured that the acid used in this experiment was in excess.

Suggest why this was essential.

1

MARKS

8. Ionic compounds that fit the formula XY, where X is the metal ion and Y is the non-metal ion, take up one of two possible cubic arrangements.

The arrangement of the ions is determined by the radius ratio, which can be calculated using the equation shown.

$$\text{Radius ratio} = \frac{\text{Ionic radius of positive ion}}{\text{Ionic radius of negative ion}}$$

The arrangements for sodium chloride and caesium chloride are shown here.

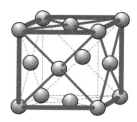

Sodium chloride

Face-centered cubic arrangement

Radius ratio below 0·8

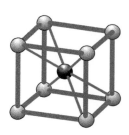

Caesium chloride

Body-centered cubic arrangement

Radius ratio above 0·8

(a) (i) Calculate the radius ratio of magnesium oxide.

You may use your data booklet to help.

1

(ii) State which cubic arrangement magnesium oxide would take.

1

(b) **Explain fully** why caesium chloride has more ionic character than sodium chloride.

2

MARKS

DO NOT
WRITE IN
THIS
MARGIN

Practice Papers for SQA Exams: Higher Chemistry Exam 3

9. August Kekulé was an organic chemist born in Germany in 1829. His work involved predicting the structure of organic compounds. One of the structures he worked on was the structure of benzene (C_6H_6).

The equation for the formation of benzene from carbon and hydrogen is shown.

$$6C(s) + 3H_2(g) \longrightarrow C_6H_6(\ell)$$

(a) Use the enthalpies of combustion shown to calculate the enthalpy of formation of benzene.

$$C_6H_6(\ell) + 7\tfrac{1}{2}O_2(g) \longrightarrow 6CO_2(g) + 3H_2O(\ell) \quad \Delta H = -3628 \text{ kJ mol}^{-1}$$

$$C(s) + O_2(g) \longrightarrow CO_2(g) \quad \Delta H = -394 \text{ kJ mol}^{-1}$$

$$H_2(g) + \tfrac{1}{2}O_2(g) \longrightarrow H_2O(\ell) \quad \Delta H = -286 \text{ kJ mol}^{-1}$$

Show your working clearly.

2

(b) **Explain fully** why potassium chloride is soluble in water but not in benzene.

2

10. Shown below are three organic molecules.

$CH_3CH=CHCH_3$ $CH_3CH_2CHClCH_3$ $CH_3CH_2CH(OH)CH_3$

Molecule A   **Molecule B**   **Molecule C**

(a) Complete the table

Molecule	Systematic name
A	
B	2-chlorobutane
C	

2

(b) (i) Molecule C can be oxidised further to produce a new compound.

Draw the full structural formula and give the systematic name of the product.

2

(ii) Suggest a reagent that could be used to oxidise Molecule C.

1

(c) Complete the equation to show how Molecule A could be converted to Molecule B.

$CH_3CH=CHCH_3 +$ $\longrightarrow$ $CH_3CH_2CHClCH_3$

1

MARKS

DO NOT
WRITE IN
THIS
MARGIN

Practice Papers for SQA Exams: Higher Chemistry Exam 3

11. The term 'opposites attract' is commonly used to describe relationships.

Using your knowledge of chemistry, comment on how relevant this term is to chemistry.

3

12. Diphosphane is a non-polar compound with the formula P_2H_4. The compound is non-polar because the elements present in the compound have the same electronegativity.

(a) State what is meant by the term electronegativity.

1

(b) The equation for the combustion of diphosphane is

$$2P_2H_4(g) + 7O_2(g) \longrightarrow P_4O_{10}(s) + 4H_2O(\ell)$$

Calculate the volume, in cm^3, of oxygen that would be required to completely burn 30 cm^3 of diphosphane.

Show your working clearly.

1

MARKS

DO NOT
WRITE IN
THIS
MARGIN

Practice Papers for SQA Exams: Higher Chemistry Exam 3

(continued)

(c) Calculate the volume occupied by 0·99 g of diphosphane. Take the molar volume to be 24 litres mol⁻¹.

Show your working clearly.

2

13. Iodine is slightly soluble in water. When excess iodine is mixed with water the following equilibrium is established:

$$I_2(s) \ + \ aq \ \rightleftharpoons \ I_2(aq) \quad \Delta H \text{ positive}$$

The concentration of dissolved iodine was measured over a period of time and the results plotted on a graph.

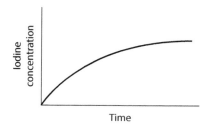

(a) Add a curve to show how the iodine concentration would change with time if the measurements were repeated at a higher temperature.

1

MARKS

DO NOT
WRITE IN
THIS
MARGIN

Practice Papers for SQA Exams: Higher Chemistry Exam 3

(continued)

(b) The dissolved iodine reacts with water as follows:

$$I_2(aq) + H_2O(\ell) \rightleftharpoons 2H^+(aq) + I^-(aq) + IO^-(aq)$$

Complete the table to show the effect of adding each of the solids on the position of equilibrium.

Solid added	Effect on equilibrium position
Potassium iodide	
Sodium hydroxide	

2

(c) (i) Iodine solution reacts with vitamin C according to the equation:

$$C_6H_8O_6(aq) + I_2(aq) \longrightarrow C_6H_6O_6(aq) + 2H^+(aq) + 2I^-(aq)$$
$$\text{(brown)} \qquad\qquad\qquad\qquad\qquad \text{(colourless)}$$

A student performed a titration with 50 cm³ of 0·1 mol l⁻¹ of vitamin C solution being added to 0·54 g of iodine in solution.

By calculating which reactant is in excess, state whether the iodine solution would have been decolourised.

Show your working clearly.

3

(ii) Apart from taking accurate measurements, suggest two points of good practice that a student should follow to ensure that an accurate end-point is achieved in a titration.

2

14. Methane reacts with chlorine in sunlight to produce a mixture of chloroalkanes in an example of a free radical chain reaction.

(a) The sunlight is required to split the chlorine molecules.

   (i)   Name the type of radiation, present in sunlight, which provides enough energy to split the chlorine molecules.

1

   (ii) Write the equation for this reaction.

1

(b) State what is meant by the term 'free radical'.

1

(c) State the names of the three stages of a free radical chain reaction.

1

(d) Many cosmetic products contain free radical scavengers.

   (i)   State what is meant by the term 'free radical scavenger'.

1

   (ii) Name another type of product that could also contain free radical scavengers.

1

15. Titanium has the highest strength-to-density ratio of any metallic element. It can be produced in an industrial process known as the Kroll process. Part of this process is shown.

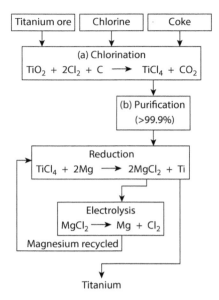

(a) Recycling is an important factor in the design of an industrial process. Magnesium is recycled in this process.

  (i) Draw an arrow onto the diagram to show how another chemical is recycled. **1**

  (ii) Name two other factors that are important influences on the design of an industrial process.

2

(b) The titanium chloride is easily separated from impurities because it is volatile.

What does this suggest about the type of bonding present in titanium(IV) chloride?

1

(c) Calculate the atom economy for this process:

$$2Mg(\ell) + TiCl_4(g) \longrightarrow 2MgCl_2(\ell) + Ti(s)$$

(continued)

MARKS

DO NOT WRITE IN THIS MARGIN

Show your working clearly.

2

16. The tables below show some of the elements from period 2 of the periodic table.

    Table 1 gives covalent (atomic) radii in pm, and table 2 gives ionic radii.

    Table 1 – Covalent radii (pm)

Na	Mg	Al	Si	P	S	Cl
154	145	130	117	110	102	99

    Table 2 – Ionic radii (pm)

Na+	Mg^{2+}	Al^{3+}	Si^{4+}	P^{3-}	S^{2-}	Cl^-
95	65	50	42	198	184	181

(a) **Explain fully** why the ions of sodium, magnesium and aluminium are significantly smaller than their atoms.

2

(b) **Explain fully** why the covalent radii of the elements decreases going from left to right across the periodic table

2

Answers to Practice Exams

Practice Exam 1

Section 1

Question	Answer	Comment	Mark
1	C	The elements with the greatest difference in electronegativity will have the greatest ionic character. Refer to page 11 of the data booklet for electronegativity values.	1
2	B	Ionisation energy is the energy required to remove one mole of electrons from one mole of atoms in the gaseous state. So always check the state symbols and ensure that only one electron has been removed.	1
3	A	'Like dissolves like.' This means that covalent substances such as carbon tetrachloride will dissolve in covalent solvents such as phosphorous chloride.	1
4	C	The activation energy on the graph is the energy difference between the peak of the graph and the reactants. The reaction is exothermic because the products have less energy than the reactants so energy must have been released.	1
5	B	Increasing the number of collisions increases the chances of successful collisions, and so the reaction rate will increase. The lower the activation energy the greater the number of particles with a kinetic energy greater than the activation energy, which again results in more successful collisions.	1
6	A	Rate is equal to 1/t so in this case $1/30 = 0.03 \text{ s}^{-1}$.	1
7	A	The carboxyl group –COOH and the ester link –COO– are highlighted.	1
8	D	A tertiary alcohol is one in which the hydroxyl functional group is attached to a carbon which is attached to three other carbon atoms.	1
9	C	The primary alcohol butan–1–ol, is oxidised to produce firstly butanal and finally butanoic acid.	1
10	C	Glycerol (propane–1,2,3–triol) is produced along with three fatty acids on hydrolysis of any fat or oil.	1
11	B	All enzymes are proteins.	1
12	C	The C–N bond is broken to allow the formation of the amine group and the carboxyl group that combine to form proteins.	1

Question	Answer	Comment	Mark
13	C	Catalysts have no effect on the position of the equilibrium but they do allow the equilibrium to establish more quickly.	1
14	C	A high pressure favours the side with the lowest gas volume and because the right hand side has no gases, a high pressure favours the production of ICl_3. The forward reaction is also exothermic and so a decrease in temperature would also increase the production of ICl_3.	1
15	A	Balance the chlorine by placing a 2 in front of the ClO_3^-. Add 6 waters to the right hand side to balance the oxygen. Finally add $12H^+$ to the left hand side to balance out the hydrogen.	1
16	B	The potassium atoms in B are losing an electron, i.e. they are being oxidised by the hydrogen.	1
17	C	10 g produces 310 kJ of energy then 60 g would produce 6 times the amount of energy ($6 \times 310 =$ 1860 kJ mol^{-1}).	1
18	B	An oxidising agent has a strong attraction for electrons and the most electronegative element is fluorine.	1
19	B	Carbon dioxide is a soluble gas, so the most accurate method to use would be S and Q as using R would result in some of the carbon dioxide dissolving in the water. P cannot be used as the gas would escape through the thistle valve.	1
20	B	The silver chloride is insoluble but the sodium chloride is soluble, so they can be separated quite easily by adding water, filtration and finally evaporation to collect the sodium chloride.	1

Practice Exam 1

Section 2

Question	Answer	Comment	Mark
1 (a)	**Type** / **Bonding and structure at room temperature** 2 — Metallic lattice solids 3 — Covalent network solids 4 — Covalent molecular gases 1 — Monatomic gases 5 — Discrete molecular solids	The bonding present in elements is responsible for the physical properties of the element such as melting point and boiling point.	2
(b)	4	Fluorine is the most electronegative element in the periodic table.	1
(c)	1	The noble gases do not form bonds due to their stable electron arrangements.	1
(d)	The atomic size increases going down a group because the atoms have more energy levels. The screening effect of these energy levels and the fact that the outer electrons are further from the nucleus results in the nucleus having less of an influence on the bonded electrons and therefore a lower electronegativity.	'**Explain clearly**' questions require you to give lots of detail in your answer to gain the 2 marks.	2
(e)	Fullerene is a covalent molecular substance whereas diamond is a covalent network.		1

Question		Answer	Comment	Mark
2	(a)		Always check that each element in the compound has the correct number of bonds, i.e. carbon = 4 bonds, nitrogen = 3 bonds and hydrogen = 1 bond.	1
	(b)	$X = 4, Y = 9, Z = 12$	A difficult equation to balance. Make sure to count all the nitrogen atoms in both reactants.	1
	(c)	$+52$ kJ mol^{-1}	**Top Tips for Hess's Law questions** 1. Remember to balance the equations. 2. Remember to reverse the enthalpy sign when reversing an equation. 3. Remember to multiply the enthalpy value when multiplying an equation. Working: You will need the balanced equations for the combustion of carbon and hydrogen. **Equation 1** $C(g) + O_2(g) \rightarrow CO_2(g)$ $\Delta H = -394$ kJ mol^{-1} **Equation 2** $H_2(g) + \frac{1}{2}O_2(g) \rightarrow H_2O(g)$ $\Delta H = -286$ kJ mol^{-1} **Equation 3** $CH_3NHNH_2(l) + 2\frac{1}{2}O_2(g) \rightarrow CO_2(g) + N_2(g) + 3H_2O(l)$ $\Delta H = -1304$ kJ mol^{-1} To match the target equation, equation 2 has to be multiplied by three and equation 3 must be reversed. The enthalpy values can then be combined $(-394 + (3 \times -286) + 1304 = 52)$.	2

Question		Answer	Comment	Mark
3		**Open question**	**Open question**	3
		3 marks: The candidate has demonstrated a good conceptual understanding of the chemistry involved. **2 marks:** The candidate has demonstrated a reasonable understanding of the chemistry involved. **1 mark:** The candidate has demonstrated a limited understanding of the chemistry involved. **0 marks:** The candidate has demonstrated no understanding of the chemistry that is relevant to the problem/situation. The candidate has made no statement(s) that is/are relevant to the problem/situation.	Open questions have no one correct answer. Listed below are *some of* the options that may be included and explained in your answer. **This list is not exhaustive and you do not have to include all of these to gain the full 3 marks.** Ensure that what you have included has been explained fully and clearly. Include diagrams, equations etc. that may help with your explanation. • Solubility of ethanoic acid in water and not oil (hydrogen bonding, polarity, electronegativity). • Solubility of salt in water and not oil (ionic bonding, polar molecules, 'like dissolves like'). • Why oil and water are not soluble (covalent bonding, polar covalent bonding, polarity, hydrogen bonding). • Roll of emulsifiers and why it is required in the vinaigrette.	
4	(a)	They only have 1 electron.	This question is problem solving and requires you to apply your knowledge of chemistry to a situation that you will not have experienced before.	1
	(b)		Refer to the diagram at the start of the question as your guide.	1
5	(a)	(i) Sulfur atoms have a greater nuclear charge than magnesium atoms and therefore have a greater attraction for the outer electrons, decreasing the radius of the atom.	The patterns of the periodic table can be learned, but to achieve an 'A' grade you must also be able to clearly explain the patterns.	2

Question		Answer	Comment	Mark
	(ii)	$Mg(g) \longrightarrow Mg^+(g) + e^-$	The first ionisation enthalpy is the energy required to remove **one** mole of electrons from one mole of atoms in the **gaseous state**.	1
(b)		232.1 kg	**Worked answer** Step 1 Work out the moles of magnesium using moles = mass ÷ formula mass. (100000/24·3 = 4115·2 moles) Step 2 The ratio is 1:1 so 4115·2 moles of magnesium would produce 4115·2 moles of magnesium sulfide. Step 3 Calculate the theoretical mass of magnesium sulfide produced using Mass = moles × formula mass (4115·2 × 56·4 = 232 098 g or 232·1 kg)	2
6	(a)	Lead is in excess.	**Top tip for questions involving N = C × V** Remember that the volume must be in litres. Change cm³ into litres by dividing by 1000. Step 1 Establish the molar ratio. One mole of lead reacts with two moles of hydrochloric acid. Step 2 Calculate the moles of each reactant using moles = mass ÷ formula mass and N = C × V. Moles of lead = (10·36 ÷ 207·2 = 0·05 moles). Moles of acid = (1 × 0·05 = 0·05 moles). Step 3 Use the ratio to establish the moles of each reactant required, e.g. 1 mole of Pb reacts with two moles of HCl, so 0·05 moles of Pb would react with 0·1 moles of HCl. This means that the Pb is in excess.	2
(b)		0·05 g	Using the balanced equation, 0·05 moles of acid (don't use lead as it is in excess!) reacts to produce 0·025 moles of hydrogen gas. Then use mass = moles × formula mass to get the answer.	1

Question	Answer	Comment	Mark
(c)	water	Markers assess these questions by asking 'Would the experiment work as drawn?'	1
7	Ethanol molecules are held together by hydrogen bonds due to the polarised –O–H group. This occurs due to the difference in electronegativity between the hydrogen and oxygen atoms. The polarised –OH group also allow ethanol to form hydrogen bonds with water molecules, making ethanol soluble in water. Propane molecules are held together by London Dispersion forces, which are much weaker than hydrogen bonds. London Dispersion forces are due to momentary displacement of electrons between atoms. Propane is insoluble in water because it is non polar and therefore is not soluble in a polar solvent such as water.	Questions like these provide an opportunity for you to tell the examiner all that you know about hydrogen bonding and London Dispersion forces.	4

Question		Answer	Comment	Mark
8		**Open question** **3 marks:** The candidate has demonstrated a good conceptual understanding of the chemistry involved. **2 marks:** The candidate has demonstrated a reasonable understanding of the chemistry involved. **1 mark:** The candidate has demonstrated a limited understanding of the chemistry involved. **0 marks:** The candidate has demonstrated no understanding of the chemistry that is relevant to the problem/situation. The candidate has made no statement(s) that is/are relevant to the problem/situation.	**Open question** Open questions have no one correct answer. Listed below are *some* of the options that may be included and explained in your answer. **This list is not exhaustive and you do not have to include all of these to gain the full 3 marks.** Ensure that what you have included has been explained fully and clearly. Include diagrams, equations etc. that may help with your explanation. • Esters present in soap may hydrolyse in the presence of water (ester link, hydrolysis, carboxylic acid, alcohols, uses of esters, uses of terpenes). • Mechanism of soap (hydrophobic, hydrophilic, emulsion).	3
9	(a)	$2CH_3OH + 3O_2 \longrightarrow 2CO_2 + 4H_2O$	The CH_3OH equation must be multiplied by 2 to provide the 12 electrons required to cancel out the 12 electrons in the other equation.	1
	(b) (i)	−482 kJ	**Worked answer** *Step 1* Calculate the energy required to break the bonds in the reactants. Two hydrogen molecules ($2 \times 436 = 872$). One oxygen molecule ($1 \times 498 = 498$). Total = 1370 kJ. *Step 2* Calculate the energy released on the formation of the OH bonds in water. Two water molecules ($4 \times -463 = -1852$). *Step 3* Combine the two to get the final answer: $1370 + (-1852) = -482$ kJ.	2

Question		Answer	Comment	Mark
	(ii)	The use of methanol as a fuel would produce carbon dioxide.		1
10 (a)	(i)	A standard solution is a solution of accurately known concentration.		1
	(ii)	The standard solution is prepared by fully dissolving the potassium permanganate in water in a beaker and transferring the contents to a standard flask. The beaker should be washed with water and the washings also transferred to the standard flask. The flask should then be made up to the meniscus with water.	Preparation of a standard solution is an essential skill for any chemist.	2
(b)	(i)	3 mol l^{-1}	**Worked answer** *Step 1* Establish the molar ratio. Five moles of Fe^{2+} ions react with one mole of MnO$_4^-$ ions. *Step 2* Calculate the moles of permanganate ions using N = C × V (0·2 × 0·025 = 5 × 10^{-3}). *Step 3* Use the ratio to establish the moles of Fe^{2+} ions used (5 × 10^{-3} × 5 = 0·025 moles of Fe^{2+}). *Step 4* Calculate the concentration of the iron(II) sulphate solution using C = N ÷ V (0·025 ÷ 0·00835 = 2·99 mol l^{-1}).	3
	(ii)	$MnO_4^-(aq) + 8H^+ + 5e^- \longrightarrow Mn^{2+}(aq) + 4H_2O$	Four water molecules are added to balance the oxygen atoms. Hydrogen ions are added to the left-hand side to balance out the hydrogen atoms. Electrons are then added to balance out the electrical charges.	1
(c)		44·4 %	**Worked answer** If 30 g provides 3·6 mg then 100 g provides 12 mg (100 ÷ 30 × 3·6 = 12). RDA is 27 mg so percentage of RDA is 44·4 % (12 ÷ 27 × 100 = 44·4 %).	2

Question		Answer	Comment	Mark
11	(a)	−299 kJ mol^{-1}	Points to remember: • 100 cm^3 of water is equal to 0·1 kg. • All combustion reactions are exothermic and ΔH should therefore have a negative sign. **Worked answer** *Step 1* Calculate the enthalpy change using ΔH = cmΔT (4·18 × 0·1 × 10 = −4·18 kJ mol^{-1}). *Step 2* Calculate the moles of ethanol used using moles = mass ÷ formula (0·64 ÷ 46 = 0·014 moles). *Step 3* Use this to calculate the enthalpy for one mole using 0·014 moles produces −4·18 kJ mol^{-1} so one mole produces (1 ÷ 0·014 × −4·18 = −299 kJ).	3
	(b)	29717 kJ kg^{-1}	If 46 g (one mole) releases −1367 kJ of energy then 1000 g releases 29 717 kJ of energy. (1000 ÷ 46) × 1367 = 29 717	1
12	(a)	Stage 5	A difficult question. You must study the diagram carefully. The arrow on the x-axis shows the potential energy increasing so a release of energy would go down the scale.	1
	(b)	Na(s) + ½Cl$_2$(g) ⟶ Na$^+$Cl$^-$(s)		1
13	(a)	82·4 %	**Worked answer** *Step 1* Establish the molar ratio. One mole of calcium carbonate reacts to produce one mole of calcium sulfate. *Step 2* Calculate the moles of CaCO$_3$ using moles = mass ÷ formula mass (490 ÷ 100·1 = 4·9 moles). *Step 3* Use the ratio to establish the moles of CaSO$_4$ produced, e.g. one mole of CaCO$_3$ produces one mole of CaSO$_4$ so 4·9 moles of CaCO$_3$ would produce 4·9 moles of CaSO$_4$. *Step 4* Using mass = moles × formula mass, calculate the theoretical mass of CaSO$_4$ produced. (4·9 × 136·2 = 667·38 tonnes.) *Step 5* Calculate the percentage yield using % yield = (actual mass ÷ theoretical mass) × 100. ((550 ÷ 667·38) × 100 = 82·4 %.)	3

Question		Answer	Comment	Mark
(b)		68·7 %	**Worked answer**	2
			Step 1 Calculate the formula mass of H_2SO_4 (98·1) and add to the formula mass of $CaCO_3$ (100).	
			Step 2 Calculate the % atom economy using % atom economy = mass of desired product ÷ mass of reactants × 100 (136·2 ÷ (98·1 + 100·1) × 100 = 68·7 %).	
14	(a)	Terpenes		1
	(b)	2-methylbuta–1,3-diene	Learn the systematic name and the structure of isoprene.	1
	(c) (i)	Molecules that can react with free radicals to form stable molecules and prevent chain reactions.		1
	(ii)	Initiation, propagation and termination.	Learn how to identify each type of reaction from an equation.	1
15	(a)	0·025 s^{-1}	Rate is equal to 1 ÷ time = (1 ÷ 40 = 0·025).	1
	(b)	Peptide link	All enzymes are proteins and therefore contain a peptide link.	1
	(c)		Markers assess these questions by asking 'Would the experiment work as drawn?'	2
16	(a)	Carbonyl functional group.	Practice drawing and naming all the functional groups in the course.	1
	(b)	Heptan-2-ol		1

Question		Answer	Comment	Mark
(c)	(i)	Hydrolysis	Learn the names of all reactions. Construct a table with the headings 'Reaction' and 'Description' and complete with all the reactions encountered throughout the course.	1
	(ii)		Remove the CO_2 to leave you with methylamine.	1
(d)	(i)	Spot 3		1
	(ii)	Differences in the polarity and/or size of molecules result in different Rf values for different compounds.	Chromatography is an excellent analytical tool.	1
17 (a)		To increase the surface area.	The greater the surface the more efficient the catalyst will be.	1
(b)	(i)	**Answers may include:** • Low cost of reactants. • Exothermic reaction, so the energy released could be used in other processes. • Costs are less as low pressure is used. • Costs are lower as reaction is exothermic, which results in less energy being required.	The atom economy of this process is low and so this is not an acceptable answer here.	2
	(ii)	A low pressure favours the side of the equilibrium with the lowest gas volume, so a low pressure would favour the production of NO.		2
	(iii)	$K = \dfrac{[NO]^4[H_2O]^6}{[NH_3]^4[O_2]^5}$	Read this carefully as it provides all the information required to answer it correctly.	2

Question	Answer	Comment	Mark
(iv)	1·02 litres Units must be correctly stated in this answer, as they are not provided in the question.	**Worked answer** *Step 1* Establish the molar ratio. One mole of copper nitrate reacts to produce two moles of nitrogen dioxide. *Step 2* Calculate the moles of $Cu(NO_3)_2$ using moles = mass ÷ formula mass (4 ÷ 187·5 = 0·0213 moles). *Step 3* Use the ratio to establish the moles of NO_2 produced, e.g. one mole of $Cu(NO_3)_2$ produces two moles of NO_2, so 0·0213 moles of $Cu(NO_3)_2$ would produce 0·0426 moles of NO_2. *Step 4* If one mole is equal to 24 litres then 0·0426 moles is equal to 1·02 litres (0·0426 × 24 = 1·02).	3

Practice Exam 2

Section 1

Question	Answer	Comment	Mark
1	B	The elements with the greatest difference in electronegativity will have the greatest ionic character. Refer to page 11 of the data booklet for electronegativity values.	1
2	C	E_a for the reverse reaction is the difference between points c and b.	1
3	D	An increase in temperature increases the kinetic energy of the particles, which results in more successful collisions.	1
4	B	Learn all the patterns of the periodic table and be able to explain why these changes occur.	1
5	B	Elements can only contain pure covalent or metallic bonding, and oxides of metals would be ionic and therefore not be a gas at room temperature.	1
6	B	Ammonia is a polar molecule due to the polar bonds and its lack of symmetry.	1
7	D	Page 11 of the data booklet contains the ionisation energies of selected elements. Combine the first and second ionisation energies for the elements to get the answer.	1
8	D	Ketones contain a carbonyl group that is not on an end carbon.	1
9	B	As well as knowing the systematic name of glycerol, you should be able to draw its structural formula.	1
10	D	Fats are more saturated than oils and this results in them having a higher boiling point.	1
11	A	Always draw out the full structural formula on scrap paper as it makes the identification of isomers simpler.	1
12	D	Learn the names of all reactions. Construct a table with the headings 'Reaction' and 'Description' and complete with all the reactions encountered throughout the course.	1
13	B	Oxidation of a secondary alcohol produces a ketone.	1
14	B	Equilibrium is established when the concentration of the reactants and products is constant but not necessarily equal.	1
15	C	A change in pressure affects reactions in which there is a difference in the moles of gas present between the reactants and products.	1
16	A	The tin changes oxidation state from Sn^{2+} to Sn^{4+}.	1

Question	Answer	Comment	Mark
17	C	20 cm^3 of methane would react to produce 20 cm^3 of carbon dioxide, but the oxygen must also be taken into consideration. 40 cm^3 would be used up reacting with the methane, leaving an excess of 60 cm^3. So the total gas volume left is 80 cm^3 (60 oxygen and 20 carbon dioxide).	1
18	A	Reaction X plus the value of ΔH_3 would equal the value of ΔH_1. So the value of X is equal to $\Delta H_1 - \Delta H_3$.	1
19	A	Combine the energy required to break all the bonds of the reactants and subtract the energy released when all the bonds form for the product.	1
20	D	The retention time (Rf) is the time taken to travel through apparatus such as a gas chromatograph, or the distance travelled in paper chromatography.	1

Practice Exam 2

Section 2

Question		Answer	Comment	Mark
1	(a)		The two peptide links are highlighted in the structure. As part of your studying make a list of all functional groups and their names.	1
	(b)		Three possible answers for this question. Ensure that you have included all the hydrogen atoms.	1

Question	Answer	Comment	Mark
(c)	The body cannot make all the amino acids required for body proteins and is dependent on dietary protein for supply of certain amino acids known as essential amino acids.		1
2 (a)	Electronegativity is a measure of the attraction an atom involved in a bond has for the electrons of the bond.	Learn all the patterns of the periodic table and be able to explain why these changes occur.	1
(b)	The atomic size is increasing going down a group as the atoms have more energy levels. The screening effect of these energy levels, and the fact that the outer electrons are further from the nucleus, results in the nucleus having less of an influence on the bonded electrons and therefore a lower electronegativity.	'Explain clearly' questions require you to give lots of detail in your answer to gain the 2 marks.	2
(c)	Covalent radius decreases going across the periodic table. This is due to the increase in the atomic charge of the element resulting in the nucleus having a greater influence over the electrons in the atom.		2
(d)	Lithium has a smaller covalent radius than sodium and therefore the nucleus has a greater influence over the outer electron, making it more difficult to remove. OR Sodium has an extra energy level and the screening effect of the extra energy level results in the nucleus having less of an influence over the outer electron, making it easier to remove.	The patterns of the periodic table can be learned, but to achieve an 'A' grade you must also be able to clearly explain the patterns.	2

Question		Answer	Comment	Mark
3	(a)		Any of these diagrams would be accepted as long as they are labelled and would 'work as drawn'.	2
	(b)	An increase in temperature increases the kinetic energy of the particles, resulting in more particles with a kinetic energy greater that the activation energy, therefore more successful collisions occur.	Temperature is a measure of the average kinetic energy of the particles, so an increase in temperature is an increase in the kinetic energy of the particles.	2
	(c)		The line must be to the right of the line labelled T_1.	1
4	(a)	Citric acid is a polar molecule as it contains polar hydroxyl functional groups, which can form hydrogen bonds with water molecules, which are also polar.	'Like dissolves like', meaning polar solutes dissolve in polar solvents and non-polar solutes dissolve in non-polar solvents.	2
	(b) (i)	Methyl hexanoate	The position of the $C=O$ bond gives a clear indication of which part of the molecule came from the parent carboxylic acid.	1

Question		Answer	Comment	Mark
	(ii)	58.6 g	**Worked answer** Remember that all esterification reactions are a 1:1 ratio. *Step 1* Work out the moles of alcohol using moles = mass ÷ formula mass ($22 \cdot 2/32 = 0 \cdot 69$ moles). *Step 2* The ratio is 1:1 so 0·69 moles of alcohol would produce 0·69 moles of ester. *Step 3* Calculate the theoretical mass of ester produced using mass = moles × formula mass ($0 \cdot 69 \times 130 = 90 \cdot 18$ g). *Step 4* Multiply the theoretical yield by 65 % ($90 \cdot 18 \times 65$ % = 58·6 g).	3
5	(a)	$Zn \longrightarrow Zn^{2+} + 2e^-$	The ion-electron equations are in your data booklet.	1
	(b)	16·9 %	**Worked answer** *Step 1* Calculate the formula mass of $CaCO_3$ (100·1) and add to the formula mass of Zn (65·4). *Step 2* Calculate the formula mass of the desired product, carbon monoxide (28). *Step 3* Calculate the % atom economy using % atom economy = mass of desired product ÷ mass of reactants × 100 ($28 ÷ (65 \cdot 4 + 100 \cdot 1) \times 100 = 16 \cdot 9$ %).	2
	(c)	 CaCO₃(s) stage 1 HCl(aq) stage 2 limewater	Ensure that the diagram is clear, large and labelled. A common mistake here is the length of the delivery tubes in stage two. Ensure that the one on the left is longer than the one on the right and dips into the limewater or the experiment would not work.	2

Question		Answer	Comment	Mark
6	(a)	Compound X and Compound Y (structures shown) OR (alternative structure shown)	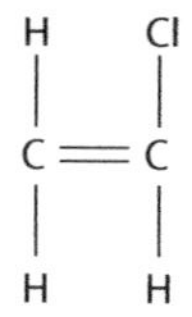 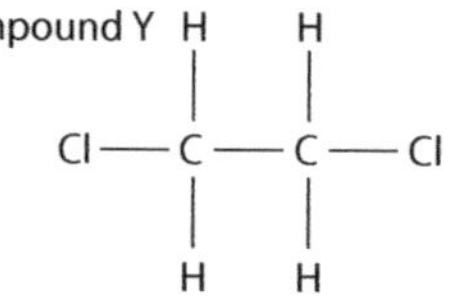 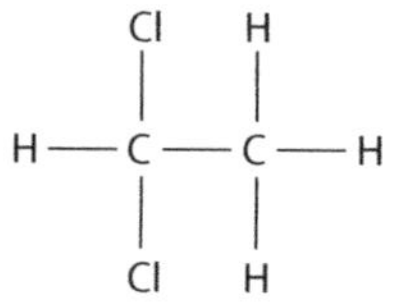 It makes no difference if the chlorine atoms are pointing up, down or to the sides.	2
	(b)	Compound A is ethanal and compound B is ethanoic acid.	Ethanol is a primary alcohol and so will oxidise to produce an aldehyde which can be oxidised further to a carboxylic acid.	2
	(c)	+227 kJ	**Worked answer** You will need the balanced equations for the combustion of carbon and hydrogen. **Equation 1** $C_2H_2(g) + 2\frac{1}{2}O_2(g) \rightarrow 2CO_2(g) + H_2O(\ell)$ $\Delta H = -1301$ kJ mol^{-1} **Equation 2** $C(g) + O_2(g) \rightarrow CO_2(g)$ $\Delta H = -394$ kJ mol^{-1} **Equation 3** $H_2(g) + \frac{1}{2}O_2(g) \rightarrow H_2O(g)$ $\Delta H = -286$ kJ mol^{-1} To match the target equation, equation 1 must be reversed and equation 2 must be multiplied by 2. The enthalpy values can then be combined $(1301 + (2 \times -394) + (-286) = 227)$.	2

Question		Answer	Comment	Mark
7	(a)	*Substance* D C A B	The properties of substances have always been a regular question in Higher Chemistry exams.	2
	(b)	Methanol has a hydroxyl group which is polar and can therefore form hydrogen bonding, which is the strongest type of van der Waals force. Ethane is non-polar and so can only form London Dispersion forces, which are much weaker than hydrogen bonding. This results in ethane having a lower boiling point than methanol.	It is important to give as much detail as possible in the 'explain' questions.	3
8	(a)	Fats have a higher degree of saturation than oils, which allows the fat molecules to pack closer together, allowing the formation of more/greater/stronger intermolecular forces, resulting in a higher melting point.		2
	(b)	Esters	All fats and oils can be classed as ester due to the presence of the ester link.	1
	(c)	12·7g	**Worked answer** *Step 1* Calculate the moles of sodium using moles = mass ÷ formula mass (0·1 ÷ 23 = 0·0043 moles). *Step 2* Establish the moles of sodium chloride. 0·0043 moles of sodium is equal to 0·0043 moles of sodium chloride because of the formula mass NaCl. *Step 3* Calculate the mass of NaCl in 10 g of margarine using mass = moles × formula mass (0·0043 × 58·5 = 0·25 g). *Step 4* Multiply by 50 to calculate the mass of salt in 500 g.	2

Question		Answer	Comment	Mark
9		**Open question** **3 marks:** The candidate has demonstrated a good conceptual understanding of the chemistry involved. **2 marks:** The candidate has demonstrated a reasonable understanding of the chemistry involved. **1 mark:** The candidate has demonstrated a limited understanding of the chemistry involved. **0 marks:** The candidate has demonstrated no understanding of the chemistry that is relevant to the problem/situation. The candidate has made no statement(s) that is/are relevant to the problem/situation.	**Open question** Open questions have no one correct answer. Listed below are *some* of the options that may be included and explained in your answer. **This list is not exhaustive and you do not have to include all of these to gain the full 3 marks.** Ensure that what you have included has been explained fully and clearly. Include diagrams, equations etc. that may help with your explanation. • Difficult to discover. (Unreactive, full outer energy levels, stable.) • Different boiling points. (London Dispersion forces, atomic size, periodic trends.) • Names linked to difficulty in discovering the elements.	3
10	(a) (i)	To provide the H^+ ions.	A very simple question when you know the answer.	1
	(ii)	The permanganate ions are purple but the manganese ions are colourless so a colour change occurs without an indicator (self-indicating reaction).		1
	(b)	0·158 mol l^{-1}	**Top tip for redox titration calculations** Remember never to include the first (rough) titration in your average. *Step 1* Establish the molar ratio. Two moles of MnO_4 reacts with five moles of H_2O_2 (it is easier to use the ratio of 1:2·5). *Step 2* Calculate the moles of permanganate ions using $N = C \times V$ ($0·1 \times 0·0158 = 1·58 \times 10^{-3}$). *Step 3* Use the ratio to establish the moles of H_2O_2 used ($1·58 \times 10^{-3} \times 2·5 = 3·95 \times 10^{-3}$ moles of H_2O_2). *Step 4* Calculate the concentration of the permanganate solution using $C = N \div V$ ($3·95 \times 10^{-3} \div 0·025 = 0·158$ mol l^{-1}).	3

Question		Answer	Comment	Mark
11		**Open question** **3 marks:** The candidate has demonstrated a good conceptual understanding of the chemistry involved. **2 marks:** The candidate has demonstrated a reasonable understanding of the chemistry involved. **1 mark:** The candidate has demonstrated a limited understanding of the chemistry involved. **0 marks:** The candidate has demonstrated no understanding of the chemistry that is relevant to the problem/situation. The candidate has made no statement(s) that is/are relevant to the problem/situation.	**Open question** Open questions have no one correct answer. Listed below are *some* of the options that may be included and explained in your answer. **This list is not exhaustive and you do not have to include all of these to gain the full 3 marks.** Ensure that what you have included has been explained fully and clearly. Include diagrams, equations etc. that may help with your explanation. • Hydrolysis reactions (the breaking down of a compound using water). • Proteins (peptide links being broken down to form amino acids, fibrous proteins). • Soap (soluble in water, hydrophobic, hydrophilic, contains esters). • Fats/grease (esters, broken down to form glycerol and fatty acids, 1:3 ratio). • Sodium hydroxide (solubility in water, catalyst for the hydrolysis of esters).	3
12	(a) (i)	The forward reaction is endothermic.	An increase in temperature favours an endothermic reaction.	1
	(ii)	An increase in pressure will favour the reverse reaction because it has the lowest gas volume. There are 2 moles of reactant gases and 4 moles of product gases.	It is important to give as much detail as possible in the *explain* questions.	2
	(iii)	A catalyst has no effect on the position/ composition of the equilibrium.	Catalysts allow equilibrium to be established more quickly but do not affect the position of the equilibrium.	1
	(b) (i)	Ketones.	The –CHO indicates the compound is an aldehyde and their isomers are the ketones.	1

Question		Answer	Comment	Mark
	(ii)	Butanone.	Always check when drawing structures that every carbon has formed four bonds only.	2
	(iii)	Butene or but-1-ene or but-2-ene.	A tricky one that requires a bit of thought. Did you remember to include the carbons from the carbon dioxide?	1
(c)	(i)	Esterification/condensation.	There are many reaction types that you must learn for Higher Chemistry. Construct a table listing them all with a description as a study aid.	1
	(ii)			1
	(iii)	Fragrances/solvents/flavouring.		1
13	(a)	Covalent.	The properties of the compounds dictate the type of bonding contained within a substance. Do not assume that it is ionic because it contains a metal and a non-metal.	1
(b)	(i)	Carbon.	The reducing agent is oxidised.	1
(b)	(ii)	79·2 litres.	**Worked answer** Step 1 Establish the molar ratio. One mole of cassiterite reacts to produce one mole of carbon dioxide. Step 2 Calculate the moles of SnO_2 using moles = mass ÷ formula mass ($500 ÷ 150 \cdot 7 = 3 \cdot 3$ moles). Step 3 Use the ratio to establish the moles of CO_2 produced, e.g. 1 mole of SnO_2 produces 1 mole of CO_2, so 3·3 moles of SnO_2 would produce 3·3 moles of CO_2. Step 4 If one mole is equal to 24 litres then 3·3 moles is equal to 79·2 litres ($3 \cdot 3 \times 24 = 79 \cdot 2$).	3

Question		Answer	Comment	Mark
14		Both have a similar radius ratio. Magnesium oxide has a radius ratio of 0·51 and the radius ratio of sodium chloride is 0·56.	Make sure to use the ionic radii, which are on page 17 of the data booklet, and not the covalent radii. The question is an 'explain fully' question and so the numbers should be quoted. You should also include the working for any calculations you performed.	2
15	(i)	$\Delta H = Y - X$	The enthalpy change is the difference in energy between reactants and products.	1
	(ii)	Adding a catalyst.	A catalyst lowers the activation energy.	1
(b)		The collision geometry must be correct or there is not enough energy to overcome the repulsion of the outer electrons.	The particles must collide facing the correct way in order to form the activated complex.	1
(c)		H————I H————I	The activated complex is a highly unstable arrangement that only exists for a fraction of a second.	1
16	(a)	Initiation, propagation and termination.		1
(b)		Ultraviolet radiation.	UV radiation provides the energy required to break down the CFCs.	1
(c)		A highly reactive atom due to the presence of an unpaired electron.	Free radicals are highly reactive because they contain an unpaired electron.	1
(d)		$\bullet Cl + O_3 \longrightarrow O_2 + ClO$	The free radicals break down the ozone to form oxygen.	1
(e)		Free radical scavengers.	These 'mop up' the free radicals.	1

Practice Exam 3

Section 1

Question	Answer	Comment	Mark
1	C	The enthalpy change is the difference in energy between the reactants and products.	1
2	A	Only a catalyst can affect the activation energy, and an increase in temperature increases the kinetic energy of the particles, resulting in more successful collisions.	1
3	D	The bonds between the molecules (intermolecular bonds) are broken during melting and, because water is polar, it is hydrogen bonds that are broken.	1
4	D	Learn the periodic trends and be able to explain the patterns.	1
5	C	The first ionisation energy is the energy required to remove one mole of electrons from one mole of atoms in the gaseous state.	1
6	C	The atomic charge is responsible for the difference in covalent radius between sodium and chlorine. The atomic charge is due to the protons in the nucleus.	1
7	B	Fullerenes are covalent molecular substances.	1
8	B	A tricky one. Use the balanced equation to establish how much oxygen reacts and how much carbon dioxide is produced. Don't include the water, as it is not a gas at room temperature.	1
9	B	Count the carbons! 3,3-dimethylbutan-1-ol has six carbon atoms and it is only compound B that also has six.	1
10	A	It is important to learn all the names of the functional groups and be able to draw them out. Construct a table of them all and test yourself.	1
11	B	Ketones cannot be oxidised further.	1
12	C	A tertiary alcohol is one in which the hydroxyl functional group is attached to a carbon atom that has no hydrogen atoms attached to it.	1
13	A	Find the position of the C=O bond as this allows you to identify the acid section of the ester.	1
14	D	When proteins are denatured they change shape.	1
15	D	Make sure that you can draw the structure of glycerol and that you know its systematic name.	1
16	B	This takes a bit of working out. Take each option one at a time and test to see if it works.	1

Question	Answer	Comment	Mark
17	A	Enthalpy is the energy released when one mole of a substance is completely burned in excess oxygen.	1
18	C	A high pressure favours the forward reaction, as there are fewer moles of gas on the right-hand side. The reaction is also exothermic, which favours lower temperatures.	1
19	C	The molar ratio is 2:3 so 0·05 moles produces 0·075 moles of oxygen which is equal to 1·8 litres (0·075 × 24).	1
20	D	Standard solutions are used in titrations and they must be prepared correctly so that they are of accurately known concentration.	1

Practice Exam 3

Section 2

Question		Answer	Comment	Mark
1	(a)	An amino acid that is required in our diet as our bodies need them to produce required proteins.		1
	(b)		Combine the two with a peptide link. Water is eliminated so the reaction is a condensation reaction. Always check that each element in the compound has the correct number of bonds, i.e. carbon = four bonds, nitrogen = three bonds and hydrogen = one bond.	1
	(c)	Peptide link.	It is important to learn the names of the functional groups and be able to draw them out. Construct a table of them all and test yourself.	1
	(d)	Change shape.	When proteins are denatured their shape is changed, resulting in them no longer functioning correctly.	1
	(e)	−214 kJ	**Worked answer** *Step 1* Calculate the energy **required** to break the bonds in the reactant molecule. Two hydrogen peroxide molecules ($1 \times 142 = 142$) for the O–O bond and ($2 \times 463 = 926$) for the two O–H bonds. Total $= 1068 \times 2 = 2136$ kJ. *Step 2* Calculate the energy **released** on the formation of water and oxygen. ($2 \times 463 = -926$) for the O–H bonds multiplied by 2 as two moles are produced ($-926 \times 2 = 1852$) and ($1 \times 498 = -498$) for the O=O bond. Total $= -2350$ kJ. *Step 3* Combine the two to get the final answer: $2136 + (-2350) = -214$ kJ.	3

Question		Answer	Comment	Mark
2	(a)	Fullerenes – covalent – molecular. Diamond – covalent – network		1
	(b)	**Open question** **3 marks:** The candidate has demonstrated a good conceptual understanding of the chemistry involved. **2 marks:** The candidate has demonstrated a reasonable understanding of the chemistry involved. **1 mark:** The candidate has demonstrated a limited understanding of the chemistry involved. **0 marks:** The candidate has demonstrated no understanding of the chemistry that is relevant to the problem/ situation. The candidate has made no statement(s) that is/are relevant to the problem/situation.	**Open question** Open questions have no one correct answer. Listed below are *some of* the options that may be included and explained in your answer. **This list is not exhaustive and you do not have to include all of these to gain the full 3 marks.** Ensure that what you have included has been explained fully and clearly. Include diagrams, equations etc. that may help with your explanation. • Oxidation (oxidising agents, copper(II) oxide, vitamin C, colour-change diagram of how this could be performed, indicators). • Detection for proteins/vitamin C in food (biuret reagent, why proteins are required, why vitamin C is required). • Description of how experiments can be performed safely and accurately. • Oxidising agents (Benedict's reagent, copper(II) oxide, colour changes).	3
3	(a) (i)	Glycerol or propane-1,2,3-triol.		1
	(ii)	Hydrolysis.	Fats are broken down into glycerol and fatty acids by hydrolysis.	1
	(b)	Oils have a higher degree of unsaturation, resulting in them being unable to pack closely together and therefore they form fewer bonds between molecules, resulting in lower melting points.	Remember to include diagrams in your explanation if you think it may help the examiner understand your answer.	2
	(c)	Esters.	All fats and oils contain the –COO– functional group.	1
4	(a)	Catalyst.	Catalysts lower the activation energy but have no effect on the enthalpy change.	1
	(b)	Activated complex.	The activated complex is a highly unstable arrangement formed between the reactant molecules.	1

Question		Answer	Comment	Mark
	(c)	Negative.	The reaction is classed as exothermic as the products have less energy than the reactants.	1
	(d)	The activation energy is the minimum energy required to overcome the repulsion caused by the outer electrons to allow collisions to take place between the atoms.	**'Explain fully'** questions require you to give lots of detail in your answer to gain the 2 marks.	2
5	(a)	Incomplete combustion or loss of ethanol due to evaporation when performed in the school lab.	Evaluation of any experiment is an essential skill for any chemist.	1
	(b)	-1345 kJ mol^{-1}	**Top tips for questions involving $\Delta H = cm\Delta T$** 1. Remember that 100 cm^3 of water is 0·1 kg. 2. Remember that all combustion reactions are exothermic and ΔH should therefore have a negative charge. **Worked answer** *Step 1* Calculate the enthalpy change using $\Delta H = cm\Delta T$ (4·18 × 0·4 × 16·1 = $-26\cdot9$ kJ mol^{-1}). *Step 2* Calculate the moles of ethanol used using moles = mass ÷ formula (0·92 ÷ 46 = 0·02 moles). *Step 3* Use this to calculate the enthalpy for one mole using 0·02 moles produces $-26\cdot9$ kJ mol^{-1} therefore one mole produces (1 ÷ 0·02 × $-26\cdot9$ = -1345 kJ mol^{-1}).	3
6	(a)	U^{4+} in UF$_4$ or uranium.	The magnesium is being oxidised to produce Mg^{2+} ions, so the uranium in UF$_4$ is the oxidising agent by accepting the electrons that magnesium has lost.	1
	(b)	To prevent the magnesium reacting with oxygen.	Magnesium would undergo combustion with oxygen at this temperature.	1
	(c)	Covalent molecular.	The low melting point is a clear indication that the bonding is covalent and the structure is molecular.	2

Question		Answer	Comment	Mark
7	(a)		Markers assess these questions by asking 'Will the experiment work as drawn?' Ensure that the diagram is clearly labelled and not too small.	2
	(b)	25 litres	**Worked answer** *Step 1* Establish the molar ratio. One mole of magnesium reacts to produce one mole of hydrogen gas. *Step 2* Calculate the moles of Mg using moles = mass ÷ formula mass ($0.2 \div 24.3 = 0.008$ moles). *Step 3* Use the ratio to establish the moles of H_2 produced, e.g. one mole of Mg produces one mole of H_2, so 0·008 moles of Mg would produce 0·008 moles of H_2. *Step 4* If 0·008 moles of H_2 is equal to 0·2 litres, then one mole is equal to 25 litres ($1 \div 0.008 \times 0.2 = 25$ litres).	3
	(c)	To ensure that all the magnesium had reacted.	If the reaction did not go to completion then the results would not be accurate.	1
8	(a)	(i)	0·51	Page 17 of the data booklet contains the ionic radii of selected elements. The ionic radii of magnesium ions is 72 and oxygen is 140 ($72 \div 140 = 0.51$).	1
		(ii)	Face-centered cubic.	The radius ratio is below 0·8 and therefore magnesium oxide is face-centered cubic.	1
	(b)		Caesium chloride has more ionic character because of the large difference in electronegativity between caesium and chlorine. Sodium and chlorine have less of a difference in electronegativity and so it is not as far along the bonding continuum as caesium chloride.	The bonding continuum diagram could also be included here to further explain your answer.	2

Question	Answer	Comment	Mark
9 (a)	406 kJ mol^{-1}	**Top tips for Hess's Law questions** 1. Remember to balance the equations. 2. Remember to reverse the enthalpy sign when reversing an equation. 3. Remember to multiply the enthalpy value when multiplying an equation. **Worked answer** You will need the balanced equations for the combustion of carbon and hydrogen. **Equation 1** $C(g) + O_2(g) \longrightarrow CO_2(g)$ $\Delta H = -394$ kJ mol^{-1} **Equation 2** $H_2(g) + \frac{1}{2}O_2(g) \longrightarrow H_2O(g)$ $\Delta H = -286$ kJ mol^{-1} **Equation 3** $C_6H_6(l) + 7\frac{1}{2}O_2(g) \longrightarrow 6CO_2(g) + 3H_2O(l)$ $\Delta H = -3628$ kJ mol^{-1} To match the target equation, equation 1 has to be multiplied by 6, equation 2 must be multiplied by 3 and equation 3 must be reversed. The enthalpy values can then be combined $(6 \times -394) + (3 \times -286) + 3628 = 406$	2
(b)	Potassium chloride is an ionic compound, soluble in polar solvents such as water. Benzene is non-polar because it contains carbon and hydrogen only and therefore potassium chloride would not be soluble in it.	'Like dissolves like' is not enough of an explanation here and the reasons for solubility must be explained clearly.	2

Question		Answer	Comment	Mark
10	(a)	Molecule A – but-2-ene Molecule B – butan-2-ol	Always check that you have the correct punctuation and that the functional group is numbered to give the lowest number possible.	2
	(b) (i)	Butanone. 	No number is required for the functional group here as the carbonyl group can only be on the second carbon.	2
	(ii)	Any suitable oxidising agent (see options in next column).	You could have included: • Hot copper(II) oxide • Benedict's reagent • Tollens' reagent • Acidified potassium permanganate • Acidified potassium dichromate	1
	(c)	$C_4H_8 + HCl \longrightarrow C_4H_9Cl$		1
11		**Open question** **3 marks:** The candidate has demonstrated a good conceptual understanding of the chemistry involved. **2 marks:** The candidate has demonstrated a reasonable understanding of the chemistry involved. **1 mark:** The candidate has demonstrated a limited understanding of the chemistry involved. **0 marks:** The candidate has demonstrated no understanding of the chemistry that is relevant to the problem/situation. The candidate has made no statement(s) that is/are relevant to the problem/situation.	**Open question** Open questions have no one correct answer. Listed below are *some of* the options that may be included and explained in your answer. **This list is not exhaustive and you do not have to include all of these to gain the full 3 marks.** Ensure that what you have included has been explained fully and clearly. Include diagrams, equations etc. that may help with your explanation. • Hydrogen bonding (electronegativity, polar molecules, polar covalent bonds). • London Dispersion forces (temporary dipole, weakest Van der Waals force). • Van der Waals forces (hydrogen bonding, permanent dipole to permanent dipole). • Ionic bonding (bonding continuum). • Electrolysis.	3

Question		Answer	Comment	Mark
12	(a)	Electronegativity is a measure of the attraction an atom has for electrons in a bond.	Fluorine is the most electronegative element in the periodic table.	1
	(b)	105 cm³	The ratio of 2:7 results in 30 cm³ requiring 105 cm³ of oxygen.	1
	(c)	0·36 l	**Worked answer** *Step 1* Calculate the moles of P_2H_4 using moles = mass ÷ formula mass (0·99 ÷ 66 = 0·015 moles). *Step 2* If 1 mole is equal to 24 litres then 0·015 moles is equal to 0·36 litres (0·015 × 24 = 0·36).	2
13	(a)	 Iodine concentration / Time	The rate of the reaction would increase as the reaction is endothermic which favours an increase in temperature.	1
	(b)	Potassium iodide would move the equilibrium to the left. Sodium hydroxide would move the equilibrium to the right.	Potassium iodide would move the equilibrium to the left as a result of the increase in concentration of iodide ions. Sodium hydroxide would move the equilibrium to the right, as the sodium hydroxide would remove the H^+ ions and so the equilibrium would shift to the right to replace the H^+ ions that have been removed.	2

Question		Answer	Comment	Mark
(c)	(i)	The solution would be decolourised as the vitamin C is in excess.	**Top tip for questions involving** **N = C × V** Remember that the volume must be in litres. Change cm^3 into litres by dividing by 1000. Step 1 Establish the molar ratio. One mole of vitamin C reacts with one mole of iodine. Step 2 Calculate the moles of each reactant using moles = mass ÷ formula mass and $N = C \times V$. Moles of iodine = $(0.54 ÷ 253.8 = 0.002$ moles). Moles of vitamin C = $(0.1 \times 0.05 = 0.005$ moles). Step 3 Use the ratio to establish the moles of each reactant required, e.g. one mole of vitamin C reacts with one mole of I_2, so 0.005 moles of vitamin C would react with 0.005 moles of I_2. This means that the vitamin C is in excess and therefore the iodine would have been decolourised.	3
	(ii)	• All glassware is clean and has been rinsed with the solution to be used. • Ensure that no chemicals are running down the outside of the burette. • White paper under the flask to easily identify the end-point. • All readings taken at eye level.	This list is not exhaustive and there are other acceptable answers.	2
14	(a)	(i)	Ultraviolet radiation (UV radiation).		1
		(ii)	$Cl_2 \longrightarrow \bullet Cl + \bullet Cl$	The chlorine molecules are broken down into free radicals.	1
	(b)	A particle with an unpaired electron.	The unpaired electron is what makes free radicals so reactive.	1
	(c)	Initiation, propagation and termination.		1
	(d)	(i)	Substances that 'mop up' free radicals and prevent further reactions.	Free radical scavengers provide an electron to the free radicals, stopping them from reacting further.	1
		(ii)	Foods.	Some foods also contain free radical scavengers to prevent them from going 'off' as quickly.	1

Question			Answer	Comment	Mark
15	(a)	(i)	Titanium ore, Chlorine, Coke → (a) Chlorination $TiO_2 + 2Cl_2 + C \longrightarrow TiCl_4 + CO_2$ → (b) Purification (>99·9%) → Reduction $TiCl_4 + 2Mg \longrightarrow 2MgCl_2 + Ti$ → Electrolysis $MgCl_2 \longrightarrow Mg + Cl_2$, Magnesium recycled → Titanium	The chlorine could also be recycled to make the process more economic.	1
		(ii)	Factors influencing process design include: • availability, sustainability and cost of feedstock(s) • opportunities for recycling • energy requirements • marketability of by-products; product yield. Environmental considerations include: • minimising waste • avoiding the use or production of toxic substances • designing products which will biodegrade if appropriate.	Your answer does not have to include all of these but you should make a note of all the possible answers as part of your studying.	2

Question	Answer	Comment	Mark
(b)	Covalent	Volatile substances have low boiling points, so the type of bonding will be covalent, most likely pure covalent.	1
(c)	20·1 %	**Worked answer** *Step 1* Calculate the formula mass of $TiCl_4$ (189·9) and add to the formula mass of two moles of Mg (24·3 × 2 = 48·6). *Step 2* The formula mass of the desired product, titanium, is 47·9. *Step 3* Calculate the % atom economy using % atom economy = mass of desired product ÷ mass of reactants × 100 (47·9 ÷ (48·6 + 189·9) × 100 = 20·1 %).	2
16 (a)	They have lost all of their outer electrons to form ions and as a result have one less energy level than their equivalent atoms, making them smaller. For example, sodium has the electron arrangement of 2,8,1 but a sodium ion (Na^+) has the electron arrangement of 2,8.	Learn all the patterns of the periodic table and be able to explain why these changes occur.	2
(b)	The covalent radii decrease going across a period because the atomic charge is increasing, resulting in the nucleus having a greater influence over the outer electrons and reducing the size of the atom.	'**Explain fully**' questions require you to give lots of detail in your answer to gain the 2 marks.	2